THE LANGUAGE GYM

FRENCH SENTENCE BUILDERS

A lexicogrammar approach

PRIMARY

Edited by:

Lou Smith

 **THE LANGUAGE GYM**

About the authors

Aurélie Lethuilier has taught for 22 years and has been at her current school for 20 years (16 years as Curriculum Leader for Modern Languages). She is very passionate about teaching and learning and loves creating resources that will get the best out of students. She has been using and testing the EPI approach for a few years now and has successfully implemented it amongst her dedicated team of amazing teachers, without whom this journey would not have been possible.

Simona Gravina has taught for 15 years, in schools in Italy and the UK, both in state and independent settings. She lives in Glasgow, Scotland. She is fluent in three languages and gets by in a few more. Simona is, besides a teacher, a mum, a bookworm, a passionate traveller and a fitness enthusiast. In the last couple of years she has been testing and implementing E.P.I. in one of the top independent schools in Scotland, St Aloysius'College, where she is currently Modern Languages Curriculum Leader in the Junior School.

Stefano Pianigiani is currently teaching languages at Temple Moor High School in Leeds, England. He teaches Spanish, Italian and French being fluent in four languages and he is also learning others. In addition he is an educator at Nuestra Escuela Leeds, the first supplementary Spanish school in Yorkshire. Stefano is a fervent creator of resources whose greatest passions are cooking and DIY. He has a wide cultural experience having studied and lived in Italy, Spain and England. He has recently completed his MA in Education at Leeds Trinity University reinforcing his knowledge and competence on how to arouse engagement adopting the communicative approach within the classroom. He is an enthusiastic educator who has fully embraced Dr Conti's teaching from its origins. His academic interest has led him to becoming a governor at St. Nicholas Catholic Primary School.

Gianfranco Conti taught for 25 years at schools in Italy, the UK and in Kuala Lumpur, Malaysia. He has also been a university lecturer, holds a Master's degree in Applied Linguistics and a PhD in metacognitive strategies as applied to second language writing. He is now an author, a popular independent educational consultant and a professional development provider. He has written around 2,000 resources for the TES website, which have awarded him the Best Resources Contributor in 2015. He has co-authored the best-selling and influential book for world languages teachers, "The Language Teacher Toolkit", "Breaking the sound barrier: Teaching learners how to listen", in which he puts forth his Listening As Modelling methodology and "Memory: what every language teacher should know". Last but not least, Gianfranco has created the instructional approach known as E.P.I. (Extensive Processing Instruction).

Dylan Viñales has taught for 15 years, in schools in Bath, Beijing and Kuala Lumpur in state, independent and international settings. He lives in Kuala Lumpur. He is fluent in five languages, and gets by in several more. Dylan is, besides a teacher, a professional development provider, specialising in E.P.I., metacognition, teaching languages through music (especially ukulele) and cognitive science. In the last five years, together with Dr Conti, he has driven the implementation of E.P.I. in one of the top international schools in the world: Garden International School. Dylan authors an influential blog on modern language pedagogy in which he supports the teaching of languages through E.P.I.

 **THE LANGUAGE GYM**

DEDICATION

For my son Horatio
-Aurélie

For my daughter Giulia
-Simona

For my family & Deirdre Jones
-Stefano

For Catrina
-Gianfranco

For Ariella & Leonard
-Dylan

 **THE LANGUAGE GYM**

Acknowledgements

Creating a book is a time-consuming yet rewarding endeavour.

Aurélie would like to thank her son Horatio, currently a primary school pupil, for his incredible patience and Christian for the endless cups of tea. Huge thanks as well to Lou and Dylan for their very constructive feedback and advice on the tasks and presentation.

Simona would like to thank her daughter Giulia, currently a Primary student, for all her encouragement and for actively testing and giving feedback on the tasks. Huge gratitude to her twin Primary teacher Emanuela for feedback on specific tasks.

Stefano is indebted to his English mother Maria who has offered her constant help in the choice of words and correct use of the language. He would also like to thank his eagle-eyed pupils at Temple Moor High School for their full engagement and enthusiasm in experimenting with the tasks.

We would like to thank our editor, Lou Smith, for her tireless work, proofreading, editing and advising on this book. She is a talented, accomplished professional who works at the highest possible level and adds value at every stage of the process. Not only this, but she is also a lovely, good-humoured colleague who goes above and beyond, and makes the hours of collaborating a real pleasure. Merci beaucoup.

Our sincere gratitude to all the people involved in the recording of the Listening audio files: Lorène (Martine), Victoria & Benjamin Carver, Steeve & Johan Duflots, Sophie Barré, Ronan Jezequel and Julien Barrett. Your energy, enthusiasm and passion come across clearly in every recording and is the reason why the listening sections are such a successful and engaging resource, according to the many students who have been alpha and beta testing the book.

Thanks to Flaticon.com and Mockofun.com for providing access to a limitless library of engaging icons, clipart and images which we have used to make this book more user-friendly than any other Sentence Builders predecessor, with a view to being as engaging as possible for primary level students.

Finally, our gratitude to the MFL Twitterati for their ongoing support of E.P.I. and the Sentence Builders book series. In particular a shoutout to our team of incredible educators who helped in checking all the units: Margot Isabelle Torres, Joanna Asse-Drouet, Nadim Cham, Sophie Barré, Corinne Lapworth, Joe Barnes Moran, Lorène Carver, Simona Gravina, Jérôme Nogues, Verónica Palacín, Tom Ball and Steve Smith. It is thanks to your time, patience, professionalism and detailed feedback that we have been able to produce such a refined and highly accurate product.

Merci,
Simona, Stefano, Gianfranco, Dylan & Aurélie

 **THE LANGUAGE GYM**

Introduction

Hello and welcome to the first Sentence Builders workbook designed for Primary aged children, designed to be an accompaniment to a French Extensive Processing Instruction course. The book has come about out of necessity, because such a resource did not previously exist.

How to use this book if you have bought into our E.P.I. approach

This book was originally designed as a resource to use in conjunction with our E.P.I. approach and teaching strategies. Our course favours flooding comprehensible input, organising content by communicative functions and related constructions, and a big focus on reading and listening as modelling. The aim of this book is to empower the beginner learner with linguistic tools - high-frequency structures and vocabulary - useful for real-life communication. Since, in a typical E.P.I. unit of work, aural and oral work play a huge role, this book should not be viewed as the ultimate E.P.I. coursebook, but rather as a **useful resource** to **complement** your Listening-As-Modelling and Speaking activities.

Sentence Builders – Online Versions

Please note that all these sentence builders will be available in bilingual and French only versions on the Language Gym website, available to download, editable and in landscape design optimised for displaying in the classroom, via the ***Locker Room** section.

*Please note that the Locker Room is only accessible via a paid subscription or as part of a full Language Gym Licence.

How to use this book if you don't know or have NOT bought into our approach

Alternatively, you may use this book to dip in and out of as a source of printable material for your lessons. Whilst our curriculum is driven by communicative functions rather than topics, we have deliberately embedded the target constructions in topics which are popular with teachers and commonly found in published coursebooks.

If you would like to learn about E.P.I. you could read one of the authors' blogs. The definitive guide is Dr Conti's "Patterns First – How I Teach Lexicogrammar" which can be found on his blog (www.gianfrancoconti.com). There are also blogs on Dylan's wordpress site (mrvinalesmfl.wordpress.com) such as "Using sentence builders to reduce (everyone's) workload and create more fluent linguists" which can be read to get teaching ideas and to learn how to structure a course, through all the stages of E.P.I.

Examples of E.P.I. activities and games to play in class, based on MARS EARS sequence, can be found in Simona's padlet (https://en-gb.padlet.com/simograv/svi55fluxeolisi9) "MFL Teaching based on E.P.I. approach, Videos and blogs, Sample activities from Modelling to Spontaneity". These can be used to model tasks.

The book "Breaking the Sound Barrier: Teaching Learners how to Listen" by Gianfranco Conti and Steve Smith, provides a detailed description of the approach and of the listening and speaking activities you can use in synergy with the present book.

 THE LANGUAGE GYM

The structure of the book

This book contains 10 units which concern themselves with a specific communicative function, such as 'I can say my name and age', 'I can talk about the weather', 'I can say what's in my town'. You can find a note of each communicative function in the Table of Contents. Each unit includes:

- a sentence builder modelling the target constructions, introduced by questions to guide communication;
- a set of Listening-As-Modelling activities to train decoding skills, sound awareness, speech-segmentation, lexical-retrieval and parsing skills;
- a set of reading tasks focusing on both the meaning and structural levels of the text;
- a set of translation tasks aimed at consolidation through retrieval practice;
- a set of writing tasks targeting essential writing micro-skills such as spelling, functional and positional processing, editing and communication of meaning.

Each sentence builder at the beginning of a unit contains one or more constructions which have been selected with real-life communication in mind. Each unit is built around that construction <u>but not solely on it</u>. Based on the principle that each E.P.I instructional sequence must move from modelling to production in a seamless and organic way, each unit expands on the material in each sentence builder by embedding it in texts and graded tasks which contain both familiar and unfamiliar (but comprehensible and learnable) vocabulary and structures. Through lots of careful recycling and thorough and extensive processing of the input, by the end of each unit the student has many opportunities to encounter and process the new vocabulary and patterns with material from the previous units.

Alongside the units you will find: No Snakes No Ladders tasks created to practise speaking skills with an engaging and fun board game that can be photocopied and played in groups of 3 students.

Important *caveat*

1) This is a '**no frills**' book. This means that there are a limited number of illustrations. This is because we want every single little thing in this book to be useful. We have given serious thought to both **recycling** and **interleaving**, in order to allow for key constructions, words and grammar items to be revisited regularly so as to enhance exponentially their retention.

2) **Listening** as modelling is an essential part of E.P.I. The listening files for each listening unit can be found in the AUDIO section on Language-Gym.com - a subscription to the website is **not required** to access these.

3) **All content** in this booklet matches the content on the **Language Gym** website. For best results, we recommend a mixture of communicative, retrieval practice games, combined with Language Gym games and workouts, and then this booklet as the follow-up, either in class or for homework.

4) This booklet is suitable for **beginner** learners. This equates to a **CEFR A1-A2** level, or a beginner **KS2 (or a less strong KS3)** class. You do not need to start at the beginning, although you may want to dip in to certain units for revision/recycling. You do not need to follow the booklet in order, although many of you will, and if you do, you will benefit from the specific recycling/interleaving strategies. Either way, all topics are repeated frequently throughout the book.

We do hope that you and your students will find this book useful and enjoyable.

Table of Contents

THE LANGUAGE GYM

UNIT 1

JE M'APPELLE

In this unit you will learn how to say in French:

- ✓ What your name is
- ✓ How old you are
- ✓ Hello and good morning
- ✓ Numbers 1 to 12

Salut! Comment tu t'appelles?

Je m'appelle Claire.

THE LANGUAGE GYM

UNIT 1. JE M'APPELLE
I can say my name and age

> ## Comment tu t'appelles? *What's your name?*
> ## Quel âge as-tu? *How old are you?*

Salut! *Hi!*	Je m'appelle *My name is*	Anne	et *and*	j'ai *I have**	un *1*	an *year*
		Claude				
		David				
		Denise			deux 2	ans *years*
		Fabien			trois 3	
Bonjour! *Good morning!* *Hello!*		Guillaume			quatre 4	
		Irène			cinq 5	
		Joseph			six 6	
		Jean			sept 7	
		Juliette			huit 8	
		Marie			neuf 9	
		Nadège			dix 10	
		Patricia			onze 11	
		Pierre			douze 12	
		Robert				
		Sophie				

*Author's note: In French you do not say *I am five years old* but *I have 5 years.* e.g. *J'ai cinq ans*

 THE LANGUAGE GYM

Unit 1. My name and age: LISTENING

1. Listen and complete with the missing vowel.

a. je m'_a_ppelle

b. _a_s-tu?

c. s_i_x

d. s_e_pt

e. qu_a_tre

f. d_i_x

g. douz_e_

h. onz_e_

i. c_o_mment

j. t_u_

| a | e | i | o | u |

2. Break the flow: draw a line between words.

a. Salut! Je m'appelle Anne et j'ai six ans.

b. Bonjour! Je m'appelle Charlotte.

c. Salut! Je m'appelle Philippe. J'ai huit ans.

d. Salut! Je m'appelle Joseph. J'ai douze ans.

e. Salut! Je m'appelle Marie. Comment t'appelles?

f. Quel âge as-tu? J'ai sept ans.

I havze

 THE LANGUAGE GYM

3

3. Listen and tick one option for each sentence. ✓

		1	2	3
a.	Je m'appelle	Pierre	Patrice	Patricia
b.	J'ai	onze ans	deux ans	quatre ans
c.	J'ai	dix ans	douze ans	huit ans
d.	Salut!	Bonjour!	Quel âge as-tu?	Comment tu t'appelles?

4. Complete with the missing syllables in the box below. ✏

a. Comment tu t'ap__ __ __ les?

b. Je __ ' __ __ pelle Vanessa.

c. __ ' __ __ cinq ans.

d. Bon__ __ __ __!

e. Sa__ __ __! Je m'appelle Joseph.

f. Quel âge __ __ -tu?

g. J'ai __ __ __ __ ans.

h. J'ai __ __ __ __ ans.

i. Je m'appelle Guil__ __ __me.

j. __ __lut! Je m'appelle Sophie.

| huit   jour   as   j'ai   pel   sa   m'ap   lut   sept   lau |

5. Listen and fill in the grid with the correct information.

	Name	Age (Number)
a.		
b.		
c.		
d.		

THE LANGUAGE GYM

6. Faulty Echo

Underline the word which sounds faulty.
e.g. J'ai <u>six</u> ans.

a. J'ai neuf ans.

b. Salut! J'ai douze ans.

c. Bonjour! Je m'appelle Marie.

d. Salut! J'ai onze ans.

e. Salut! Je m'appelle Guillaume

et j'ai huit ans.

f. Je m'appelle Jean.

g. Quel âge as-tu?

7. Track the sounds

Listen and write down how many times you will hear the sound.

1.	a	
2.	e	
3.	i	
4.	o	
5.	u	

8. Spot the Intruder

Identify and underline the word(s) in each sentence the speaker is NOT saying.

e.g. Je m'appelle Anne <u>salut</u>.

a. Comment tu t'appelles? Je ne m'appelle pas Pierre.

b. Quel âge as-tu? J'ai trois six ans.

c. Bonjour! J'ai Je m'appelle Béatrice.

d. Salut Joseph! Et quel âge as-tu?

e. Salut! Deux je m'appelle Benjamin et j'ai dix ans.

THE LANGUAGE GYM

9. Spelling Challenge (1-12)
Listen and complete the French words with the missing letter.

a.	d__ux	g.	__uit
b.	u__	h.	t__ois
c.	s__x	i.	qua__re
d.	ne__f	j.	se__t
e.	c__nq	k.	do__ze
f.	di__	l.	o__ze

10. Listen and circle the correct number (1-12).
e.g. Quel âge as-tu? J'ai neuf ans.

e.g.	7	8	9
a.	6	7	8
b.	10	3	2
c.	9	12	11
d.	4	5	1
e.	12	6	4

Unit 1. My name and age: VOCABULARY BUILDING

1. Match Up

1. je m'appelle	a. ten	1	
2. dix	b. four	2	
3. trois	c. two	3	
4. quatre	d. five	4	
5. deux	e. my name is	5	
6. huit	f. seven	6	
7. onze	g. three	7	
8. ans	h. eight	8	
9. cinq	i. years	9	
10. sept	j. eleven	10	

2. Broken Words

a. j'____   I have

b. hu_____   eight

c. s_____   six

d. a_____   years

e. je m'app____   my name is

f. dou____   twelve

g. u_____   one

h. se____   seven

i. ne____   nine

j. di_____   ten

3. Complete the sentences with the missing words below.

a. J'ai _____ ans.   *I am seven years old.*

b. Je m' _____ Dylan.   *My name is Dylan.*

c. J'ai _____ ans.   *I am eleven years old.*

d. Comment tu ___'appelles?   *What is your name?*

e. Quel âge _____?   *How old are you?*

f. _____, je m'appelle Anne.   *Hello, my name is Anne.*

g. J'ai _____ ans.   *I am twelve years old.*

h. Je m'appelle Pat et _____ treize ans.   *My name is Pat and I am 13.*

as-tu	appelle	douze	sept	t'	salut	onze	j'ai

THE LANGUAGE GYM

4. Sentence Building Blocks

Use the words in the building blocks to make a correct French sentence.

a.

ans

cinq J'ai

_____

b.

as-tu?

âge Quel

_____

c.

douze Je Jean

et j'ai ans m'appelle

_____

d.

Irène onze Je

et j'ai ans m'appelle

_____

Unit 1. My name and age: READING

1. Sylla-Bees

Translate the phrases putting the cells in the correct order.

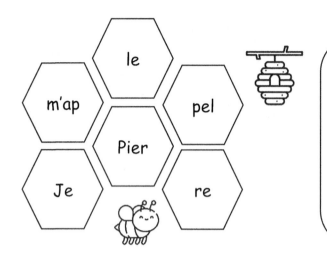

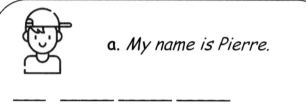

a. *My name is Pierre.*

—— —— —— ——

—— —— .

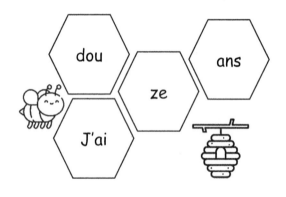

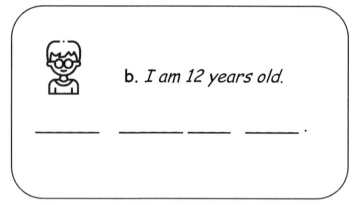

b. *I am 12 years old.*

—— —— —— —— .

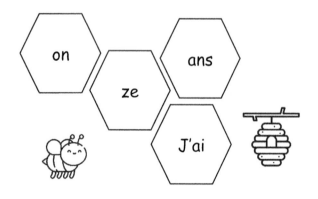

c. *I am 11 years old.*

—— —— —— —— .

2. True or False ✓

Read the dialogues below and for each statement tick.

1a. Salut! Comment tu t'appelles? Je m'appelle Fabien.

1c. J'ai dix ans. Et toi?

1b. Salut! Je m'appelle Marie. Quel âge as-tu?

1d. J'ai huit ans.

2a. Bonjour! Comment tu t'appelles? Je m'appelle Stéphane.

2c. J'ai douze ans. Et toi?

2b. Salut! Je m'appelle Amira. Quel âge as-tu?

2d. J'ai onze ans.

	True	False
1a. His name is **Fabien.**		
1b. Her name is **Martine.**		
1c. He is 11 years old.		
1d. She is 8 years old.		
2a. His name is **Paul.**		
2b. Her name is **Amira.**		
2c. He is 12 years old.		
2d. She is 10 years old.		

Unit 1. My name and age: WRITING

1. Spelling

a. j __ m' __ __ __ __ __ __ __ __   *my name is*

b. J' __ __ d __ __ a __ __.   *I am ten years old.*

c. q __ __ tre __ ns   *four years old*

d. n __ __ f a __ __   *nine years old*

e. Com __ __ __ t t __ t'a __ __ __ ll __ s?   *What's your name?*

f. Q __ __ l âge a __- t __ ?   *How old are you?*

g. J' __ __ o __ __ __ a __ __.   *I am eleven years old.*

2. Anagrams

a. iaJ' tuih nas   *I am 8 years old.*

  __'__ __ __ __ __ __ __ __ __ __ __.

b. eJ ppm'lleae ennA   *My name is Anne.*

  __ __ __'__ __ __ __ __ __ __ __ __ __ __.

c. iJ'a oeduz sna   *I am twelve years old.*

  __'__ __ __ __ __ __ __ __ __ __ __.

d. aJ'i setp sna   *I am seven years old.*

  __'__ __ __ __ __ __ __ __ __ __ __.

e. iaJ' zeno asn   *I am eleven years old.*

  __'__ __ __ __ __ __ __ __ __ __ __.

THE LANGUAGE GYM

salut   hi

3. Faulty Translation. Write the correct English version.

e.g. J'ai <u>dix</u> ans. ⟹ *I am <u>11</u> years old.* | I am 10 years old |

a. J'ai sept ans. ⟹ *I am 6 years old.* | |

b. J'ai trois ans. ⟹ *I am 13 years old.* | |

c. Quel âge as-tu? ⟹ *How do you spell it?* | |

d. Comment tu t'appelles? ⟹ *How old are you?* | |

e. Salut! Je m'appelle Ben. ⟹ *Bye! My name's Ben.* | |

4. Phrase-level Translation. How would you say it in French?

a. I am 8 years old. _____

b. My name is… _____

c. What's your name? _____

d. I am 12 years old. _____

e. How old are you? _____

f. Good morning! _____

g. Hello! _____

h. I am 10 years old. _____

UNIT 2

L'ALPHABET

In this unit you will learn to:

- ✓ Spell your name in French
- ✓ Practise French sounds

You will revisit:

- ★ Saying your name and age
- ★ How to count from 1 to 12

Comment ça s'écrit?

Aa Bb Cc

Ça s'écrit
S-A-R-A-H

THE LANGUAGE GYM

UNIT 2. ALPHABET AND DECODING SKILLS
I can hear and pronounce French sounds

Comment ça s'écrit? *How do you spell it?*

1. Listen and write the alphabet as you hear it.

Ça s'écrit

It is spelt

A	*<ah>*	O	_____
B	_____	P	_____
C	_____	Q	_____
D	_____	R [r]	_____
E [ə]	_____	S	_____
F	_____	T	_____
G	_____	U [y]	_____
H	_____	V	_____
I	_____	W	_____
J	_____	X	_____
K	_____	Y	_____
L	_____	Z	_____
M	_____		
N	_____		

2. Fill in the gaps. Comment ça s'écrit? *How do you spell it?*

a. N __ dège

b. D__ nise

c. Ro __ ert

d. Patr __ ce

e. Chr __ stine

f. Ca __ ine

g. Cora __ ie

h. Céli __ e

i. Jac __ ues

j. Va __ ér __ e

3. Complete the words with the missing letters.

a. C__mment ç__ s'écr__t?

b. Je m'__ppelle Marie.

c. Je m'a __ __ elle Benjamin.

d. __a s'écr__t...

e. J__ __'__ppelle __ean.

4. Listen and choose the correct spelling.

	1	2
a.	je m'apple	je m'appelle
b.	ans	ânes
c.	jaune	Jean
d.	anniversairy	anniversaire
e.	espagnol	espanyol
f.	Hoolie	Julie
g.	Joseph	Josep
h.	vert	verde
i.	infant	enfant
j.	Guillaume	Guiyaume

THE LANGUAGE GYM

5. Listen and tick the letter you hear.

1.	C	G	Z
2.	F	S	H
3.	L	H	J
4.	L	N	M
5.	I	E	A
6.	K	C	S
7.	X	H	V
8.	U	V	W

6. Listen and write the names being spelled out.

1. _ _ _ _ _ _   5. _ _ _ _ _

2. _ _ _ _ _ _   6. _ _ _ _ _ _ _

3. _ _ _ _   7. _ _ _ _ _ _

4. _ _ _ _ _   8. _ _ _ _ _ _

THE LANGUAGE GYM

No Snakes No Ladders

Unit 1-2

7 et	6 Je m'appelle Pierre.	5 Bonjour!	4 Comment tu t'appelles?	3 Je m'appelle Antoine.	2 Je m'appelle...
8 J'ai sept ans.	9 Je m'appelle Philippe.	10 Je m'appelle Marie.	11 J'ai onze ans.	12 J'ai neuf ans.	13 Quel âge as-tu?
23 Salut! Je m'appelle ...	22 J'ai six ans.	21 Je m'appelle Sophie.	20 J'ai cinq ans.	19 Bonjour!	18 Comment ça s'écrit?
24 Je m'appelle Joseph.	25 J'ai douze ans.	26 Je m'appelle Samuel.	27 Je m'appelle Charlotte.	28 J'ai quatre ans.	29 Salut Jean!

| 1 Salut! DÉPART | 14 J'ai huit ans. | 17 Je m'appelle Guillaume. | 16 J'ai dix ans. | 30 Bonjour Anne! | 15 Je m'appelle Patricia. ARRIVÉE |

17

THE LANGUAGE GYM

No Snakes No Ladders

DÉPART	1 Hello!	2 My name is....	3 My name is Antoine.	4 What's your name?	5 Good morning!	6 My name is Pierre.	7 and
15 My name is Patricia.	14 I am 8 years old.	13 How old are you?	12 I am 9 years old.	11 I am 11 years old	10 My name is Marie.	9 My name is Philippe.	8 I am 7 years old.
16 I am 10 years old.	17 My name is Guillaume.	18 How do you spell it?	19 Good morning!	20 I am 5 years old.	21 My name is Sophie.	22 I am 6 years old.	23 Hello! My name is...
ARRIVÉE	30 Good morning Anne!	29 Hello Jean!	28 I am 4 years old.	27 My name is Charlotte.	26 My name is Samuel.	25 I am 12 years old.	24 My name is Joseph.

UNIT 3

COMMENT ÇA VA?

In this unit you will learn how to say in French:

✓ How you are

You will revisit:

★ What is your name
★ Saying your age
★ 'Hello' and 'Good morning'

Salut! Ça va?

Ça va très bien, merci.

THE LANGUAGE GYM

UNIT 3. COMMENT ÇA VA?
I can greet people and say how I am

> ## Ça va? / Comment ça va? *How are you?*

				MASC	FEM
Salut *Hi*		**super bien** *great*			
Bonjour *Good morning /Hello*		**très bien** *very well*	**parce que je suis** *because I am*	**calme** *calm*	**calme** *calm*
				détendu *relaxed*	**détendue** *relaxed*
Bonjour *Good afternoon*		**bien** *well*		**fatigué** *tired*	**fatiguée** *tired*
Bonsoir *Good evening*	**ça va** *I am*			**heureux** *happy*	**heureuse** *happy*
		comme ci comme ça *so-so*	**parce que je ne suis pas** *because I am not*		
Bonne nuit *Good night*				**nerveux** *nervous*	**nerveuse** *nervous*
		mal *feeling bad*		**stressé** *stressed*	**stressée** *stressed*
Merci *Thank you*		**très mal** *feeling awful*		**triste** *sad*	**triste** *sad*

Unit 3. I can greet people & say how I am: LISTENING

1. Listen and tick the word you hear.

	1	2	3
e.g.	bonjour ✓	salut	bonsoir
a.	comme ci comme ça	mal	bien
b.	calme	triste	heureuse
c.	heureux	fatigué	stressé
d.	détendu	très mal	heureux
e.	nerveux	nerveuse	détendu

2. Listen and complete with the missing vowel.

a. Je suis heureus___.

b. B___nsoir!

c. Je suis c___lme.

d. B___nne nuit!

e. Ça va s___per bien.

f. Je suis tr___ste.

g. Je suis fat___gué.

h. Salut! Je m'___ppelle Robert.

i. Ça va très b___en.

j. B___njour!

k. Ça va très m___l.

l. Je suis détend___e.

m. Je suis nerveus___.

n. Sal___t!

a
e
i
o
u

 THE LANGUAGE GYM

3. Complete with the missing syllables in the box below.

a. Je suis __ __ __ __ssée.

b. Ça va __ __ __ __.

c. __ __ __ jour!

d. Bon__ __ __ __!

e. Ça va __ __ __ __ bien.

f. Ça va bien par__ __ que je suis heureux.

g. Je suis cal__ __.

h. Sa__ __ __! Je m'appelle Marie.

i. Je suis __ __tiguée.

j. Ça va mal parce que je suis __ __ __veux.

| très | stre | soir | bien | ner | ce | lut | bon | me | fa |

4. Listen and choose the correct spelling.

	1	2
a.	bonjour	bonjor
b.	je suis	je sois
c.	bonswar	bonsoir
d.	nerveux	nerfveux
e.	bein	bien
f.	heuruex	heureux
g.	calme	calm
h.	parceque	parce que
i.	ca va?	ça va?
j.	détendue	daytendue

5. Break the flow: draw a line between words.

a. Ça va bien parce que je suis heureux.

b. Ça va mal parce que je suis fatigué.

c. Salut! Ça va mal parce que je suis triste.

d. Ça va? Ça va comme ci comme ça, merci.

e. Salut! Je m'appelle Joseph. Ça va bien.

6. Fill in the grid with the correct information in English.

	Greeting	Emotion
e.g. Martine	hi	tired
a. André		
b. Daniel		
c. Jean		
d. Benoît		
e. Belle		

7. Faulty Echo

Underline the word which sounds faulty.

e.g. <u>Salut,</u> ça va très bien.

a. Bonjour, ça va comme ci comme ça.

b. Ça va bien parce que je suis heureux.

c. Ça va bien parce que je suis détendue.

d. Ça va? Ça va super bien.

e. Ça va mal parce que je suis triste.

f. Ça va super bien parce que je suis calme.

g. Bonjour, ça va très mal.

8. Spot the Intruder

Identify the word(s) in each sentence the speaker is NOT saying.

e.g. Ça va très bien, <u>merci</u>.

a. Bonsoir! Je suis calme, détendu et ça va bien.

b. Bonjour, bonsoir! Ça va comme ci comme ça parce que je suis triste.

c. Ça va super bien parce que j'ai je suis calme.

d. Salut! Ça va mal parce que je ne suis pas fatiguée.

e. Ça va? Ça va très bien.

9. Narrow Listening: gap-fill

a. Salut! Ça va _____ parce que je suis heureux.

b. _____, ça va mal parce que je suis _____.

c. Ça va bien parce que je suis _____.

d. Ça va? Ça va très bien, _____.

e. Salut! _____comme ci comme ça parce que je suis _____.

f. Ça va? Je suis _____ mais fatiguée.

THE LANGUAGE GYM

Unit 3. I can greet people & say how I am: VOCAB BUILDING

1. Match Up

1. fatigué   a. relaxed
2. détendue   b. How are you?
3. je suis   c. calm
4. triste   d. happy
5. nerveuse   e. tired
6. calme   f. I am
7. heureux   g. stressed
8. stressé   h. nervous
9. Ça va?   i. sad

1	
2	
3	
4	
5	
6	
7	
8	
9	

2. Broken Words

a. m_____   feeling bad

b. s_____ b_____   great

c. fa_____   tired

d. bi_____   well

e. bon_____   good morning

f. au r_____   goodbye

g. par____ q_____   because

h. je s_____   I am

i. t_____ bien   very well

3. Complete with the missing words.

a. Ça va _____ bien parce que je suis heureux.

   I am great because I am happy.

b. Ça ____ mal parce que je suis fatigué.

   I am feeling bad because I am tired.

c. Ça va bien _____ je suis calme.

   I'm well because I am calm.

d. Ça va comme ci comme ça parce que je suis _____.

   I'm so-so because I am sad.

e. _____? Ça va très bien parce que je suis _____.

   How are you? I am very well because I am relaxed.

va	ça va	super	triste	parce que	détendu

Unit 3. I can greet people & say how I am: READING

1. Sylla-bees
Translate the phrases putting the cells in the correct order.

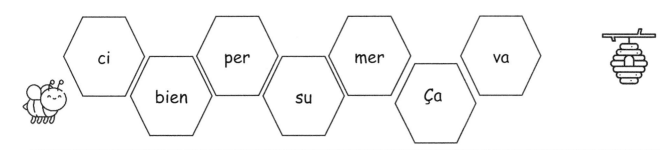

a. *I'm great, thank you.*

___ ___ ___ ___ ___ ___, ___ ___ ___.

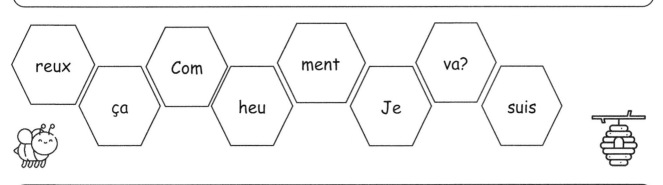

b. *How are you? I'm happy.*

___ ___ ___ ___ ___? ___ ___ ___ ___ ___.

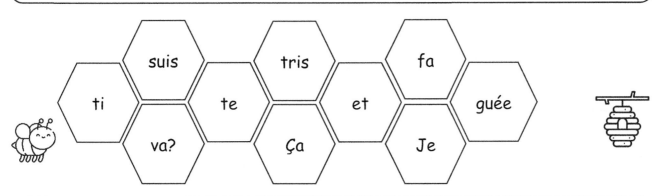

c. *How are you? I'm tired and sad (f).*

___ ___ ___? ___ ___ ___ ___ ___ ___ ___ ___.

THE LANGUAGE GYM

2. Read the sentences and complete the grid below in English.

e.g. Salut! Je m'appelle Franck. J'ai huit ans. Ça va très bien parce que je suis heureux.

c. Bonjour! Je m'appelle Lola. J'ai six ans. Ça va mal parce que je suis fatiguée.

a. Salut! Je m'appelle Houda. J'ai onze ans. Ça va super bien parce que je suis heureuse.

d. Salut! Je m'appelle Simone. J'ai neuf ans. Ça va bien parce que je suis calme.

b. Bonjour! Je m'appelle Théo. J'ai dix ans. Ça va bien parce que je suis détendu.

e. Salut! Je m'appelle Damien. J'ai douze ans. Ça va mal parce que je suis nerveux.

	Name	Age	Feeling	Reason
e.g.	Franck	8	very well	happy
a.				
b.				
c.				
d.				
e.				

Unit 3. I can greet people & say how I am: WRITING

1. Spelling

a. Ç __ v__   bi __ __.   *I am well.*

b. Ç __ v__   s__ p __ __   b__ __ n.   *I am great.*

c. pa __ ce que   j__ s__ __s   h __ u__ eux   *because I am happy*

d. parce q__ __   je su__ __   tr __ __ __ __ __   *because I am sad*

e. parce __ue   j__ s__is dé __ e __ d __   *because I am relaxed*

f. C __ m __ e __t __ a v__?   *How are you?*

g. Ç __ v__?   Ç__ v__ mal.   *How are you? I am feeling*

                                                   bad.

2. Anagrams

a. eJ uiss nrvxeeu.   *I am nervous.*

__ __   __ __ __ __   __ __ __ __ __ __ __.

b. eJ llm'peepa lPua.   *My name is Paul.*

__ __   __ __'__ __ __ __ __ __ __ __   __ __ __ __.

c. eJ isus ssétres.   *I am stressed.*

__ __   __ __ __ __   __ __ __ __ __ __ __ __.

d. eJ en ssiu spa hreeuxu.   *I am not happy.*

__ __   __ __ __   __ __ __ __   __ __ __

__ __ __ __ __ __ __.

28

THE LANGUAGE GYM

3. Faulty Translation. Spot the difference and correct with English words.

e.g. Je suis fatigué. ⟹ I am _cheerful_. | I am tired

a. Ça va très bien. ⟹ I am happy. |

b. Comment ça va? ⟹ What's your name? |

c. Je suis détendue. ⟹ I am nervous. |

d. Je suis triste. ⟹ I am calm. |

e. Bonjour! Ça va? ⟹ Bye! How are you? |

4. Phrase-level Translation. How would you say it in French?

a. I am well. _____

b. I am feeling awful. _____

c. How are you? _____

d. I am relaxed. (m) _____

e. I am stressed. (m) _____

f. I am happy. (f) _____

g. Hello! I am great. _____

h. I am calm. _____

i. I am relaxed. (f) _____

THE LANGUAGE GYM

UNIT 4

MON ANNIVERSAIRE

In this unit you will learn how to say in French:

- ✓ When your birthday is
- ✓ Numbers up to 31
- ✓ Months of the year

You will revisit:

- ★ Your name and age
- ★ Saying how you are

Quelle est la date de ton anniversaire?

Mon anniversaire est le vingt-huit mars.

THE LANGUAGE GYM

UNIT 4. MON ANNIVERSAIRE
I can say when my birthday is

Quelle est la date de ton anniversaire? *When is your birthday?*

		un *1**	an *year*
		deux *2*	
		trois *3*	
		quatre *4*	
		cinq *5*	
		six *6*	
Je m'appelle …… *I am called* ……	**J'ai** *I have*	sept *7*	**ans** *years*
		huit *8*	
		neuf *9*	
		dix *10*	
		onze *11*	
		douze *12*	
		treize *13*	
		quatorze *14*	
		quinze *15*	
	seize *16*		
	dix-sept *17*	janvier *January*	
	dix-huit *18*	février *February*	
	dix-neuf *19*	mars *March*	
	vingt *20*	avril *April*	
Mon anniversaire est le *My birthday is the*	vingt-et-un *21*	mai *May*	
	vingt-deux *22*	juin *June*	
	vingt-trois *23*	juillet *July*	
	vingt-quatre *24*	août *August*	
	vingt-cinq *25*	septembre *September*	
	vingt-six *26*	octobre *October*	
	vingt-sept *27*	novembre *November*	
	vingt-huit *28*	décembre *December*	
	vingt-neuf *29*		
	trente *30*		
	trente-et-un *31*		

*Author's note: The number "un" becomes "premier" when it comes before a month.

e.g. Mon anniversaire est le **premier** juin.

THE LANGUAGE GYM

Unit 4. I can say when my birthday is: LISTENING

1. Listen and tick the word you hear. ✓

	1	2	3
a.	six	sept	trois
b.	juin	juillet	un
c.	seize	dix-sept	dix-huit
d.	vingt-deux	vingt-quatre	vingt-neuf
e.	septembre	novembre	décembre
f.	ans	anniversaire	âge

2. Faulty Echo

Underline the word which sounds faulty, e.g., J'ai <u>six</u> ans.

a. mon anniversaire est...

b. le dix-neuf avril

c. Je m'appelle Lorène.

d. le vingt-six juin

e. le dix-huit octobre

f. J'ai onze ans.

g. le seize décembre

h. le trois mars

3. Listen and complete with the missing letters.

a. le do__ze ma__s

b. le __ __atorze févri__r

c. le tr__ __s __uillet

d. le vingt-s__x j__in

e. l__ vingt s__ptembre

f. le q__inze o__tobre

g. J'ai hu__t a__s.

h. le tr__nte janv__er

32

4. Complete with the missing syllables in the box below.

a. J'ai dou__ __ ans.

b. le vingt-__ __ __ __ septembre

c. le trente-et-un __ __ __ __let

d. mon an __ __ versaire est...

e. le __ __ __ -sept août

f. le douze __ __ __ __

g. le __ __ __ tre mars

h. le trois __ __ __ vier

i. le __ __ __ __ __-cinq mai

j. le __ __ __ __ te avril

juin	huit	qua	ni	ze	vingt	juil	dix	tren	jan

5. Break the flow: draw a line between words.

a. Monanniversaireestledix-septnovembre.

b. Jem'appelleMarie.J'aionzeans.

c. Monanniversaireestlequatreaoût.

d. Quelleestladatedetonanniversaire?Ledeuxavril.

e. Monanniversaireestlevingt-deuxmai.

f. Monanniversaireestletreizefévrier.

6. Fill in the grid with the correct date of birth.

	Day	Month
e.g.	17th	August
a.		
b.		
c.		
d.		
e.		

7. Spot the Intruder

Identify the word(s) in each sentence the speaker is NOT saying.

e.g. Mon anniversaire est le dix-sept <u>vingt</u> novembre.

a. Mon anniversaire est le dix-neuf huit septembre.

b. Mon anniversaire est le salut vingt janvier.

c. Quelle est j'ai la date de ton anniversaire?

d. Je m'appelle Pierre. Mon anniversaire est le an deux février.

e. Mon anniversaire est le quinze je m'appelle juin.

f. Mon novembre anniversaire est le trente-et-un octobre.

8. Catch it, Swap it

Listen, spot the difference between what you hear and **the written** text and edit each sentence accordingly.

e.g. Mon anniversaire est le quatre <u>janvier</u>.

août

a. Je m'appelle Jean. Mon anniversaire est le quatre août.

b. Je m'appelle André. Mon anniversaire est le six juillet.

c. Mon anniversaire est le trente-et-un octobre.

d. J'ai onze ans. Quelle est la date de ton anniversaire?

e. Je m'appelle Serge. Mon anniversaire est le treize avril.

f. J'ai douze ans. Mon anniversaire est le dix mars.

g. J'ai trois ans. Mon anniversaire est le vingt juillet.

9. Listen: tick or cross.

	✓	✗
e.g. David's birthday is the 9th of December.	✓	
a. Pierre is 13 years old.		
b. Aurélie's birthday is the 7th of June.		
c. Lorène's birthday is the 8th of May.		
d. Antoine's birthday is the 17th of November.		
e. Dylan's birthday is the 18th of October.		
f. Gianfranco's birthday is the 15th of July.		

THE LANGUAGE GYM

Unit 4. I can say when my birthday is: READING

1. Sylla-Bees
Translate the phrases putting the cells in the correct order.

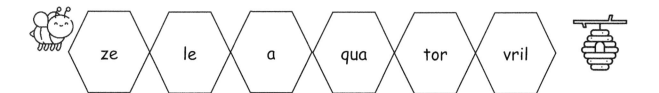

a. *the 14th of April*

_____ _____ _____ _____ _____ _____

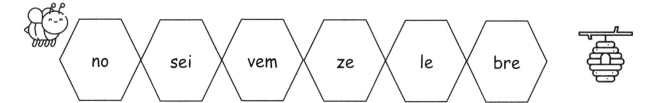

b. *the 16th of November*

_____ _____ _____ _____ _____ _____ _____

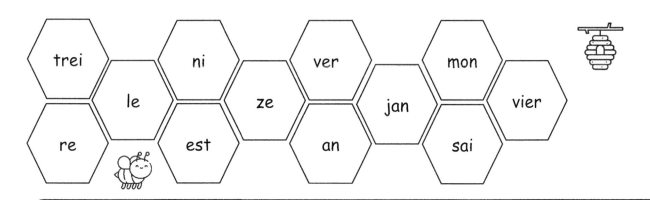

c. *My birthday is the 13th of January.*

_____ _____ _____ _____ _____ _____ _____ _____ _____ _____
_____ _____.

2. True or False
Read the paragraphs below and then answer True or False.

1. Salut! Je m'appelle Sarah Legrand. Ça va très bien parce que je suis heureuse. J'ai sept ans. Mon anniversaire est le dix-neuf septembre.

2. Salut! Je m'appelle Richard Lepetit. Ça va très mal parce que je suis fatigué. J'ai dix ans. Mon anniversaire est le vingt-et-un avril.

		True	False
1	a. Her name is **Sarah.**		
	b. She is feeling bad.		
	c. She is 6 years old.		
	d. Her birthday is the 13th of October.		
2	a. His name is **Francis.**		
	b. He is feeling awful because he is nervous.		
	c. He is 10 years old.		
	d. His birthday is the 22nd of April.		

THE LANGUAGE GYM

3. Tick or Cross

A. Put a tick if you find the words in the text or a cross if you do not find them.

Salut! Je m'appelle **Ariella**. Ça va bien parce que je suis calme. J'ai sept ans. Mon anniversaire est le quatorze février.

Salut! Je m'appelle **Lenny**. Ça va très mal parce que je suis triste. J'ai neuf ans. Mon anniversaire est le vingt-quatre juillet.

	✓	✗
a. je m'appelle		
b. douze ans		
c. Salut!		
d. ça va mal		
e. mon anniversaire est		
f. le sept février		

g. I am 7 years old.		
h. my birthday		
i. 24th of July		
j. because I am happy		
k. I am stressed		

B. Find the French in the texts above.

a. my name is… _____

b. my birthday is… _____

c. I am 7 years old _____

d. because I am calm _____

THE LANGUAGE GYM

4. Language Detective

- <u>Je m'appelle</u> **Pierre** Legrand. Ça va très bien parce que je suis heureux. J'ai douze ans. Mon anniversaire est le dix-huit avril.

- Bonjour! Je m'appelle **Véronique** Dupont. Ça va mal parce que je suis stressée. J'ai treize ans. Mon anniversaire est le quatre août.

- Salut! Je suis **Sébastien** Duval. Ça va super bien parce que je suis calme. J'ai quatorze ans. Mon anniversaire est le onze juillet.

- Bonjour! Je m'appelle **Francis** Florentin. Ça va comme ci comme ça parce que je suis fatigué. J'ai dix ans. Mon anniversaire est le trente octobre.

A. Find someone who...

a. ...is 12 years old

b. ...is tired

c. ...is happy

d. ...was born on the 11ᵗʰ of July

e. ...is 13 years old

f. ...is calm

g. ...was born on the 18ᵗʰ of April

B. Put a cross in the box and underline the corresponding French translation. One is odd.

My name is...	I am 14 years old	I am feeling bad
Good morning	my birthday	Hello, I am...
because I am stressed	I am so-so	the 30ᵗʰ October
I am great	Good afternoon	I am 11 years old

39

THE LANGUAGE GYM

Unit 4. I can say when my birthday is: WRITING

1. Spelling

a. B__ __ j __ u__!   *Good morning!*

b. m__ __   a__ __ __ ver __ __ __ re   *my birthday*

c. le t__ o__ __ no__ em __ __e   *the 3rd of November*

d. __e   __ __nq   av__ __l   *the 5th of April*

e. le tr__ __ __ __   jan__ i__ __   *the 13th of January*

f. le q__ __nze   j__ __ ll__ __   *the 15th of July*

g. J'__ __   s__ x   a __ __.   *I am 6 years old.*

2. Anagrams

a. pets toocrbe   *7th of October*

___ ___ ___ ___   ___ ___ ___ ___ ___ ___ ___

b. uetarqzo ûtao   *14th of August*

___ ___ ___ ___ ___ ___ ___   ___ ___ ___ ___

c. zeon   céebemdr   *11th of December*

___ ___ ___ ___   ___ ___ ___ ___ ___ ___ ___ ___

d. retetn niju   *30th of June*

___ ___ ___ ___ ___ ___   ___ ___ ___ ___

3. Gapped Translation

Complete the translation.

a. J'ai sept ans.   I am _____ years old.

b. J'ai six ans.   I am _____ years old.

c. Je ne suis pas fatigué.   I am not _____.

d. Je suis heureux.   I am _____.

e. le seize février   the _____ of February

f. le vingt-trois août   the _____ of August

g. Bonjour!   Good _____!

4. Match Up

a. Je m'appelle   1. le douze avril.

b. Ça va   2. onze ans.

c. J'ai   3. Pierre Duchemin.

d. Mon anniversaire est   4. je suis fatigué.

e. Ça va comme ci comme ça parce que   5. ton anniversaire?

f. Quelle est la date de   6. très bien.

a	b	c	d	e	f
3					

THE LANGUAGE GYM

5. Rock Climbing

Starting from the bottom, pick one chunk from each row to translate the sentences below.

janvier.	vingt-trois juin.	J'ai dix ans.	juillet.	le trois mai.
anniversaire est le	le cinq	Mon anniversaire est	mars.	C'est le quinze
le vingt-huit	Francis.	anniversaire ?	ans. Mon	Mon anniversaire est
Je m'appelle	J'ai douze	Mon anniversaire est	J'ai onze ans.	Quelle est la date de ton
a.	b.	c.	d.	e.

a. My name is Francis. My birthday is the 3rd of May.

_____

b. I am 12 years old. My birthday is the 23rd of June.

_____

c. My birthday is the 28th March. I am 10 years old.

_____

d. I am 11 years old. My birthday is the 5th of July.

_____

e. When is your birthday? It's the 15th of January.

_____

THE LANGUAGE GYM

6. Mosaic Translation

Use the words in the grid to help you translate the sentences below.

a.	J'ai treize	Anne.	J'ai	seize	décembre.
b.	Quel	ans. Mon	Mon anniversaire	est le	onze ans.
c.	Je m'appelle	est le trente-et-un	C'est le	J'ai	avril.
d.	Quelle est la date	âge as-tu?	anniversaire est le	douze	vingt-deux août.
e.	Mon anniversaire	de ton anniversaire?	octobre.	dix-huit	ans.

a. I am 13 years old. My birthday is the 18th of April.

_____

b. How old are you? I am 12 years old.

_____

c. My name is Anne. My birthday is the 22nd of August.

_____

d. When is your birthday? It's the 16th of December.

_____

e. My birthday is the 31st of October. I am 11 years old.

_____

43

THE LANGUAGE GYM

7. Sentence Puzzle

Put the words in the correct order.

  a. treize Mon est septembre le anniversaire.

  b. ton Quelle la de date anniversaire est?

  c. avril douze le est anniversaire Mon.

  d. Je Claude m'appelle et neuf j'ai ans.

  e. dix-neuf Mon janvier est le anniversaire.

  f. anniversaire Mon est le décembre vingt-quatre.

  g. m'appelle Je Claire et ans quatorze j'ai.

  h. Je Marie m'appelle et janvier est le mon anniversaire douze.

  i. as-tu Quel âge? sept J'ai ans.

8. Tangled Translation

a. Write the French words in English to complete the translation.

Hello, je m'appelle *Philippe*. Ça va *very well* parce que je suis *happy*. J'ai *ten*

ans. Mon anniversaire *is* le vingt *of January*. *When is* de ton anniversaire?

b. Write the English words in French to complete the translation.

Salut! *My name is* Elise. *I am* mal *because* je suis *tired*. *I am* onze *years old*.

My birthday est le huit juillet. Quelle est la date de *your birthday?*

44

9. Fill in the Gaps

a. Salut! Je _____ Alexandre. Ça va _____ parce que

_____ heureux. J'ai quatorze _____. Mon anniversaire

est le _____ octobre.

bien	quinze	ans	m'appelle	je suis

b. Salut! Je m'appelle Enzo. _____ neuf ans. Ça va mal

_____ je suis _____. Mon anniversaire _____ le vingt-

deux _____.

triste	est	j'ai	février	parce que

10. Guided Translation

a. J__ m'a_____ S_____ et j'_____ o_____ a_____.

My name is Simone and I am 11 years old.

b. Ç__ v_____ t_____ b_____ p_____ q_____ j__ s____ c_____.

I am very well because I am calm.

c. Ç__ v_____ m_____ p_____ q_____ j____ s_____ f_____.

I am feeling bad because I am tired. (f)

d. M_____ a_____ e_____ l____ q_____ a_____.

My birthday is the 15th of August.

e. Q_____ e____ l__ d_____ d__ t____ a_____?

When is your birthday?

THE LANGUAGE GYM

11. Pyramid Translation

Translate into French starting from the top. Write the sentences in the grid below.

a. Hello

b. Hello, my name is Jean.

c. Hello, my name is Jean. I am 10 years old.

d. Hello, my name is Jean. I am 10 years old. My birthday is

e. Hello, my name is Jean. I am 10 years old. My birthday is the 24ᵗʰ of October.

a.	
b.	
c.	
d.	
e.	

  **THE LANGUAGE GYM**

No Snakes No Ladders

Unit 3-4	7 Comment tu t'appelles?	8 Je suis un peu stressé.	23 Merci!	24 le vingt-six juillet
	6 parce que je suis fatigué	9 Je suis heureux.	22 J'ai neuf ans.	25 Bonjour! Ça va comme ci comme ça.
	5 Ça va comme ci comme ça.	10 Quel âge as-tu?	21 le trente-et-un octobre	26 parce que je suis calme
	4 Ça va très bien.	11 J'ai douze ans.	20 Ça va mal.	27 le trente janvier
	3 Salut! Ça va?	12 Ça va super bien.	19 Je ne suis pas triste.	28 J'ai quinze ans.
	2 J'ai douze ans.	13 parce que je suis détendue	18 Quelle est la date de ton anniver-saire?	29 Je suis heureuse.
	1 Je m'appelle Jean.	14 mais je suis nerveuse	17 le onze juin	30 Salut! Ça va très mal.
	DÉPART	15 Mon anniver-saire est...	16 le vingt mai	ARRIVÉE

47

THE LANGUAGE GYM

No Snakes No Ladders

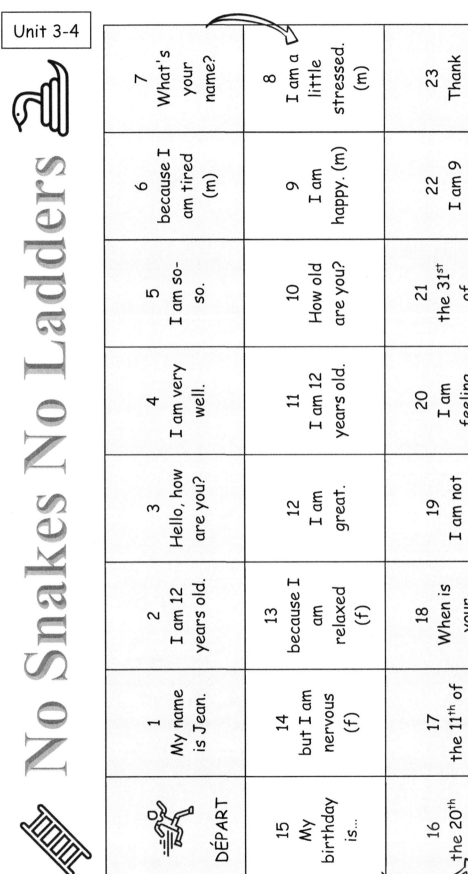

7 What's your name?	**6** because I am tired (m)	**5** I am so-so.	**4** I am very well.	**3** Hello, how are you?	**2** I am 12 years old.	**1** My name is Jean. DÉPART
8 I am a little stressed. (m)	**9** I am happy. (m)	**10** How old are you?	**11** I am 12 years old.	**12** I am great.	**13** because I am relaxed (f)	**14** but I am nervous (f)	**15** My birthday is...
23 Thank you!	**22** I am 9 years old.	**21** the 31st of October	**20** I am feeling bad.	**19** I am not sad.	**18** When is your birthday?	**17** the 11th of June	**16** the 20th of May
24 the 26th of July	**25** Good morning, I am so-so.	**26** because I am calm	**27** the 30th of January	**28** I am 15 years old.	**29** I am happy. (f)	**30** Hello! I am feeling awful. ARRIVÉE

 THE LANGUAGE GYM

UNIT 5
MON ANIMAL DOMESTIQUE

In this unit you will learn how to say in French:

✓ What pets you have at home
✓ What colour your pets are
✓ What their name is
✓ *J'ai / Tu as*
✓ *Je n'ai pas de / Tu n'as pas de*

You will revisit:

★ Saying your name
★ How to say your age and birthday

J'ai un chien.

J'ai un chat.

THE LANGUAGE GYM

UNIT 5. MON ANIMAL DOMESTIQUE
I can say what pets I have

> ## As-tu un animal? *Do you have a pet?*

J'ai *I have*			**chat** *cat* **cheval** *horse* **chien** *dog* **cochon d'Inde** *guinea pig* **hamster** *hamster* **lapin** *rabbit* **mouton** *sheep* **oiseau** *bird* **perroquet** *parrot* **pingouin** *penguin* **poisson** *fish*	**blanc** *white* **bleu** *blue* **gris** *grey* **jaune** *yellow* **marron** *brown* **noir** *black* **rouge** *red* **rose** *pink* **vert** *green*		Coco
Je n'ai pas de/d' *I do not have* *Don't use "un /* *une" afterwards*	**un** *a*	**grand** *big* **petit** *small*			**qui** **s'appelle** *who* *is called*	Dixie Loki Maya
Tu as *You have*						Pilou Perle
Tu n'as pas de/d' *You do not have* *Don't use "un /* *une" afterwards*	**une** *a*	**grande** *big* **petite** *small*	**araignée** *spider* **poule** *hen* **souris** *mouse* **tortue** *tortoise/turtle*	**blanche** *white* **bleue** *blue* **grise** *grey* **jaune** *yellow* **marron** *brown*		Rocky Zaza
Je n'ai pas d'animaux. *I don't have pets.* **Tu n'as pas d'animaux.** *You don't have pets.*				**noire** *black* **rouge** *red* **rose** *pink* **verte** *green*		

50

Unit 5. I can say what pets I have: LISTENING

1. Listen and complete with the missing vowel.

a. un ch__en

b. un ch__val

c. un ch__t

d. un poiss__n

e. une tort__e

f. un mout__n

g. un l__pin

h. une poul__

a
e
i
o
u

2. Listen and tick the word you hear.

		1	2	3
a.	J'ai	un poisson.	un oiseau.	un lapin.
b.	Je n'ai pas de	poule.	tortue.	souris.
c.	Je n'ai pas de	cheval.	chien.	chat.
d.	Tu n'as pas de	pingouin.	chien.	poisson.
e.	As-tu	une poule?	une tortue?	une araignée?

3. Complete with the missing syllables in the box below.

a. un chien mar __ __ __

b. une __ __ __ le blanche

c. un che __ __ __ gris

d. un poisson __ __ __ __

e. un la __ __ __ marron

f. une a __ __ __ gnée noire

g. un mouton __ __ __ ge

h. un __ __ __ __ gris

| rou | val | rai | ron | bleu | chat | pou | pin |

THE LANGUAGE GYM

4. Complete the words with the missing endings.

a. un oiseau jaun__

b. un mouton ros__

c. un perroquet roug__

d. un chat gri__

e. une tortue vert__

f. un chien blan__

g. un peti__ pingouin

h. une poule noir__

i. un poisson ver__

j. un cochon d'Inde marro__

5. Write the missing word as you hear it.

a. un _____ bleu

b. une _____ blanche

c. une grande _____

d. une _____ jaune

e. une souris _____

f. J'ai un _____

g. un _____ rose

h. une _____ rouge

i. Je ___'ai pas ___ chat.

j. un chien _____

k. un _____ noir

6. Faulty Echo

Underline the word which sounds faulty.

a. Je n'ai pas de pingouin gris.

b. J'ai un mouton rose.

c. Je n'ai pas de poisson bleu.

d. Je n'ai pas de petit chat.

e. Tu as une petite poule?

f. Tu n'as pas de cheval marron.

g. Tu n'as pas d'animaux.

h. J'ai une tortue verte.

i. J'ai un perroquet jaune.

j. Je n'ai pas d'araignée rouge.

52

7. Listen and choose the correct spelling.

	1	2
a.	je m'apple	je m'appelle
b.	ans	ânes
c.	Jon	Jean
d.	lapine	lapin
e.	espanyol	espagnol
f.	cinq	zinc
g.	jaune	jeune
h.	weet	huit
i.	Patricia	Patricha
j.	cheveux	cheval
k.	mouton	montagne
l.	oranger	orange

8. Fill in the grid with the correct information in English.

	pet	colour
a.		
b.		
c.		
d.		
e.		
f.		

53

9. Spot the Intruder

Identify the word in each sentence the speaker is NOT saying.

  a. J'ai un poisson bleu et un deux chat gris.

  b. As-tu un animal? Non, je n'ai pas d'animaux.

  c. Tu as un cheval blanc qui comment s'appelle Rocky.

  d. J'ai un pas grand chien marron.

  e. Tu n'as pas de grande tortue mais tu as une petite souris.

  f. J'ai un pingouin gris blanc qui s'appelle Dixie.

10. Catch it, Swap it

Listen, spot the difference between what you hear and the written text and edit each sentence accordingly.

e.g. J'ai un <u>chat</u> blanc. | mouton |

  a. Tu as un grand cheval gris.

  b. Je n'ai pas d'oiseau noir et jaune.

  c. J'ai un lapin mais je n'ai pas de mouton.

  d. Tu n'as pas de poisson bleu mais tu as une poule.

  e. As-tu un animal? Oui, j'ai un chien noir.

  f. Je n'ai pas de pingouin mais j'ai un cochon d'Inde.

  g. J'ai un petit perroquet qui s'appelle Rocky.

THE LANGUAGE GYM

11. Listening Slalom

Listen and pick the equivalent English words from each column – drawing a line as you follow the speaker.

e.g. J'ai un chat noir – *I have a black cat*

You could colour in the boxes for each sentence in a different colour and read out the sentence in French.

e.g.	**I have a**	 <!-- horse -->	blue
a.	You have a	 <!-- dog -->	**black**
b.	I don't have a	 <!-- cat -->	pink
c.	I have a	 <!-- rabbit -->	white
d.	You do not have a	 <!-- fish -->	brown
e.	I have a	 <!-- turtle -->	grey
f.	I don't have a	 <!-- mouse -->	yellow

THE LANGUAGE GYM

Unit 5. I can say what pets I have: READING

1. Sylla-Bees
Read and put the syllables in the cells in the correct order.

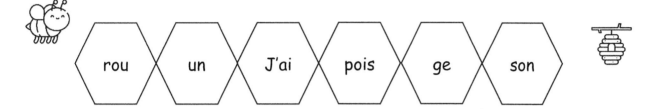

  a. *I have a red fish:* ____ __ _____ _____ _____.

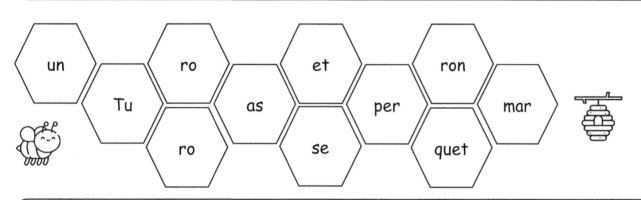

b. *You have a brown and pink parrot:* ___ ___ ___
_____ ___ _____ _____ ___ ____.

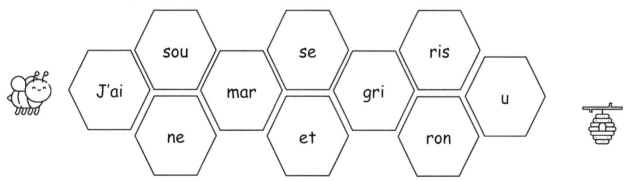

c. *I have a brown and grey mouse:* ____ __ ___ _____ _____ __ _____ ____.

2. Read, Match, Find and Colour

A. Match these sentences to the pictures above.

a. J'ai un lapin gris et rose.

b. Tu as une tortue verte et rouge.

c. J'ai un pingouin blanc et noir.

d. Je n'ai pas de poule jaune.

e. J'ai un poisson bleu et jaune.

f. J'ai un chien marron et gris.

g. Tu as un petit chat.

h. Tu n'as pas de mouton blanc et rose.

i. J'ai un perroquet rouge et bleu.

j. J'ai un grand cheval.

B. Using the sentences in task A find the French for:

a. a red parrot

b. I have a fish.

c. a grey rabbit

d. a green turtle

e. brown and grey

f. a small cat

g. a big horse

h. I have a penguin.

i. You do not have...

j. I do not have...

 THE LANGUAGE GYM

3. True or False
Read the paragraphs below and then answer True or False.

1. Salut! Je m'appelle **Eric** et j'ai dix ans. Mon anniversaire est le cinq juin. J'ai un cheval gris qui s'appelle Zagor.

2. Salut! Je m'appelle **Charlotte** et j'ai huit ans. Mon anniversaire est le treize mai. J'ai un chat blanc qui s'appelle Pilou.

		True	False
1	a. **Eric** is 10 years old.		
	b. His birthday is the 4th of July.		
	c. He has a grey dog.		
	d. His pet is called Zagor.		
2	a. **Charlotte** is 7 years old.		
	b. Her birthday is the 3rd of March.		
	c. She has a white cat.		
	d. Her cat is called Lola.		

4. Tick or Cross

A. Read the text. Tick the box if you find the words in the text, cross it if you do not find them.

- Salut! Je m'appelle **Stéphane**.

J'ai onze ans. Mon anniversaire est le dix-neuf janvier. J'ai un chat noir et blanc qui s'appelle Perle. C'est un grand chat. As-tu un animal?

- Salut! Je m'appelle **Béatrice**.

J'ai sept ans. Mon anniversaire est le douze avril. J'ai un lapin noir et blanc qui s'appelle Coco. C'est un petit lapin.

		✓	✗
a.	je m'appelle		
b.	treize ans		
c.	un grand chat		
d.	un lapin		
e.	un chien gris		
f.	qui s'appelle		

g.	I am 7 years old.		
h.	my birthday		
i.	black and brown		
j.	black and white		
k.	I have a cat.		
l.	small rabbit		

B. Find the French in the texts above.

a. my name is _____

b. my birthday is _____

c. It is a big cat. _____

d. Do you have a pet? _____

e. I have a black rabbit. _____

59

5. Language Detective

- <u>Je m'appelle</u> **Joseph**. J'ai douze ans. Mon anniversaire est le quinze février. J'ai un oiseau jaune qui s'appelle Loki mais je n'ai pas de chien noir.

- Je m'appelle **Carine**. J'ai treize ans. Mon anniversaire est le vingt janvier. J'ai une souris grise qui s'appelle Zaza mais je n'ai pas de poisson bleu.

- Salut! Je m'appelle **Emmanuel**. J'ai six ans. Mon anniversaire est le deux juin. J'ai un perroquet vert qui s'appelle Coco mais je n'ai pas de cheval blanc.

- Bonjour! Je m'appelle **Nico**. J'ai onze ans. Mon anniversaire est le quatorze mai. J'ai un cochon d'Inde marron et blanc qui s'appelle Rocky.

A. Find someone who…

a. …is 12 years old

b. …has a green parrot

c. …has a grey mouse

d. …was born on the 2nd of June

e. …does not have a black dog

f. …was born in January

g. …has a guinea pig

h. …is 11 years old

B. Put a cross in the box and underline the corresponding French translation. One is odd.

My name is	a yellow bird	brown and white
I have a guinea pig	My birthday	I am 8 years old
who is called	I don't have	15th of February
black dog	14th of May	but I don't have

Unit 5. I can say what pets I have: WRITING

1. Spelling

a. j'__ __	*I have*
b. u__ c__ __ __	*a cat*
c. __n c__ __ __ a __	*a horse*
d. un ch__ __ __ m__ __ __ o __	*a brown dog*
e. un p__ __ __ __ __ qu__t j__ __ __ __	*a yellow parrot*
f. t__ a __	*you have*
g. u__ a__ __ __ __ __	*a pet*

2. Anagrams

a. iJ'a nu nchei rnoi.   *I have a black dog.*

__'__ __ __ __ __ __ __ __ __ __ __ __ __ __ __.

b. eJ ian' psa ed thca tvre.   *I do not have a green cat.*

__ __ __'__ __ __ __ __ __ __ __ __ __ __ __ __ __ __.

c. noM mtnouo eppalls'e nBe.   *My sheep is called Ben.*

__ __ __ __ __ __ __ __ __'__ __ __ __ __ __ __ __ __.

d. aiJ' nue ttroeu lebue.   *I have a blue turtle.*

__'__ __ __ __ __ __ __ __ __ __ __ __ __ __ __ __ __.

e. iJ'a neu lpeuo rnioe.   *I have a black hen.*

__'__ __ __ __ __ __ __ __ __ __ __ __ __ __ __.

3. Gapped Translation

a. J'ai sept ans.

b. J'ai un petit chat.

c. Je n'ai pas d'araignée.

d. Tu as un cheval marron.

e. J'ai un mouton qui s'appelle Dida.

f. J'ai un cheval blanc.

g. As-tu un animal?

h. Je n'ai pas d'animaux.

i. J'ai un cochon d'Inde noir.

I am _____ years old.

I have a _____ cat.

I do not have a _____.

____ have a brown _____.

I have a sheep _____ Dida.

I _____ a white _____.

Do ____ _____ a pet?

I do not have _____.

I have a black _____.

4. Match Up

a. J'ai un

b. une tortue

c. J'ai

d. J'ai une

e. un cheval

f. Je n'ai

g. As-tu

1. blanche

2. chat.

3. un perroquet.

4. noir

5. pas d'animaux.

6. un animal?

7. poule.

a	b	c	d	e	f	g
2						

THE LANGUAGE GYM

5. Rock Climbing
Starting from the bottom, pick one chunk from each row to translate the sentences in the grid below.

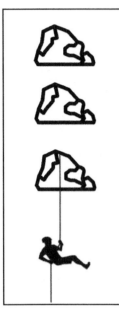

rose.	noir.	Rocky.	blanche.	marron.
tortue	poule	cheval	appelle	chat
pas de	s'	une	de petite	un grand
Mon chien	J'ai	Je n'ai	Tu as	Tu n'as pas
a.	b.	c.	d.	e.

a.	My dog is called Rocky.

b.	I have a white hen.

c.	I don't have a black cat.

d.	You have a big and brown horse.

e.	You do not have a small and pink turtle.

6. Mosaic Translation

Use the words in the grid to help you translate the sentences below.

a.	J'ai	de chat	Nadim	j'ai	Jeanne.
b.	Je n'ai pas	petite	noir	et	un perroquet.
c.	Mon mouton	un pingouin	tortue	et il est	marron.
d.	Mon chien	s'appelle	grand	noir et	blanc.
e.	J'ai une	est	mais	qui s'appelle	blanc.

a. I have a black and white penguin.

_____

b. I don't have a cat but I have a parrot.

_____

c. My sheep is called Nadim and it is white.

_____

d. My dog is big, black and brown.

_____

e. I have a small tortoise who is called Jeanne.

_____

64

7. Sentence Puzzle

Put the words in the correct order.

a. J'ai chien un marron. _____

b. un As-tu animal? _____

c. un perroquet Tu as. _____

d. J'ai chat blanc un. _____

e. poule J'ai une petite. _____

f. un bleu poisson Tu as jaune et. _____

g. J'ai blanc cochon d'Inde un. _____

h. n'ai d'animaux pas Je. _____

i. chat J'ai et blanc noir un. _____

8. Tangled Translation

a. Write the French words in English to complete the translation.

Hello, je m'appelle *Pierre. I am* sept ans. Mon anniversaire *is the* dix-huit *July.*

J'ai un *white dog* qui s'appelle *Pilou.* Il est très *big.*

b. Write the English words in French to complete the translation.

Hello, je m'appelle Bernard. *I am* neuf *years old.* Mon *birthday* est le vingt

June. I have a blue fish qui s'appelle Nemo. Il est très *small.*

9. Fill in the Gaps

a. Salut! Je m' _____ Eric et j'ai dix ans. Mon anniversaire est le
_____ juin. _____ un cheval _____ qui _____ Zar.

s'appelle	j'ai	cinq	gris	appelle

b. Salut! Je m'appelle Fred. J'ai _____ ans. Mon anniversaire est

le dix-neuf _____. J'ai un _____ marron et _____ qui

s'appelle Coby. Il est _____.

petit	chien	blanc	janvier	onze

10. Guided Translation

a. J___ m'_____ S_____ et j'_____ o_____ a_____.
My name is Stéphane and I am 11 years old.

b. J'___ u__ l_____ g_____ q___ s'_____ C_____.
I have a grey rabbit, who is called Coco.

c. J__ n'__ p___ d_ p_____, m_____ j'___ u_____ p_____.
I do not have a parrot, but I have a hen.

d. T____ a___ u____ c_____ m_____ et u___ c_____ n_____.
You have a brown dog and a black cat.

e. T__ n'__ p__ d__ t_____, m___ t____ a___ u___ a_____.
You do not have a tortoise, but you have a spider.

f. J__ n'___ p___ d__ c_____ d'_____ b_____.
I do not have a white guinea pig

66

11. Pyramid Translation

Starting from the top, translate chunks into French. Write the sentences in the box below.

a. I have

b. I have a white bird

c. I have a white bird who is called Dory

d. I have a white bird who is called Dory, but I do not have

e. I have a white bird who is called Dory, but I do not have a black guinea pig.

a.

b.

c.

d.

e.

THE LANGUAGE GYM

12. Staircase Translation

Starting from the top, translate each chunk into French.
Write the sentences in the grid below.

a.	Do you have	a dog?				
b.	I do not have	a white	sheep.			
c.	You have	a black	horse	who is called Zar.		
d.	I have	a brown	cat	and	a big tortoise.	
e.	I have	a small fish	and	you have	a grey	penguin.

Answers / Réponses

a.	
b.	
c.	
d.	
e.	

Challenge / Défi

Can you create 2 more sentences using the words in the staircase grid?

☆	
☆	

68

THE LANGUAGE GYM

UNIT 6
MON CARTABLE

In this unit you will learn how to say in French:

- ✓ What items you have in your pencil case/school bag
- ✓ What colour are your school items

You will revisit:

- ★ How to use *j'ai / tu as*
- ★ Indefinite articles *un / une*
- ★ Word order noun + adjective

J'ai une trousse blanche.

J'ai une calculatrice rouge.

69

UNIT 6. MON CARTABLE
I can say what's in my schoolbag

> Qu'est-ce que tu as dans ton cartable? *What do you have in your schoolbag?*
> Qu'est-ce que qu'il y a dans ta trousse? *What's in your pencil case?*

Dans mon cartable *In my schoolbag*	**j'ai** *I have*		**blanc** *white*
			bleu *blue*
		agenda *planner*	**gris** *grey*
		bâton de colle *glue stick*	**noir** *black*
		cahier *exercise book*	**vert** *green*
		classeur *folder*	
	il y a *there is*	**crayon** *pencil*	**jaune** *yellow*
		un *a*	**crayon de couleur** *coloured pencil*	**marron** *brown*
		livre *book*	**orange** *orange*
	je n'ai pas de *I don't have* *Don't use "un / une" afterwards*	**stylo** *pen*	**rose** *pink*
		taille-crayon *pencil sharpener*	**rouge** *red*
Dans ma trousse *In my pencil case*	**il n'y a pas de** *there isn't* *Don't use "un / une" afterwards*	**une** *a*	**calculatrice** *calculator* **gomme** *rubber* **règle** *ruler* **trousse** *pencil case*	**blanche** *white* **bleue** *blue* **grise** *grey* **noire** *black* **verte** *green* **jaune** *yellow* **marron** *brown* **orange** *orange* **rose** *pink* **rouge** *red*

THE LANGUAGE GYM

Unit 6. I can say what's in my schoolbag: LISTENING

1. Faulty Echo

Underline the word which sounds faulty.

e.g. Dans mon <u>cartable</u>, j'ai un livre.

a. Dans ma trousse, il y a un bâton de colle.

b. Qu'est-ce que tu as dans ton cartable?

c. Dans mon cartable, j'ai une calculatrice.

d. Dans ma trousse, j'ai une règle.

e. Dans mon cartable, il y a un cahier.

f. Dans ma trousse, j'ai une gomme et un stylo.

2. Listen and match.

a.	1.

b.	2.

c.	3.

d.	4.

e.	5.

f.	6.

3. Listen and tick the word you hear.

	1	2	3
e.g.	classeur ✓	calculatrice	cahier
a.	cartable	stylo	crayon
b.	agenda	trousse	livre
c.	crayon	taille-crayon	crayon de couleur
d.	j'ai	gomme	il y a
e.	bâton de colle	j'ai	il n'y a pas de

THE LANGUAGE GYM

4. Fill in the grid with the correct information in English.

		Item	Colour
e.g.	Julien	calculator	red
a.	Martine		
b.	Jacques		
c.	Théo		
d.	Valérie		

5. Listen and complete with the missing vowels.

a. une calc__latr__ce

b. un l__vre gr__s

c. un __gend__

d. un cl__sseur

e. un c__rt__ble

f. un styl__ r__se

g. un cl__sseur m__rron

h. un bât__n d__ c__lle

i. un c__rt__ble __range

j. un c__hier r__se

a
e
i
o
u

6. Complete with the missing syllables in the box below.

a. J'ai une gom __ __

b. un __ __ __yon de couleur vert

c. un agen__ __ rouge

d. un sty__ __ noir

e. une trous__ __ jaune

f. un carta__ __ __ blanc

g. J'ai un taille-crayon ro__ __.

h. une __ __ __culatrice noire

i. une __ __ __ __ __se ver__ __

j. un clas__ __ __ __ orange

| se seur da cal me se lo cra te ble trous |

* **Author's note:** Ask your teacher how many syllables there are in *"crayon"*. Officially there is only one, but many French speakers say there are two. ☺

72

THE LANGUAGE GYM

7. Break the flow: draw a line between words.

a. Dansmatrousse,ilyaunbâtondecollegris.

b. Dansmatrousse,ilyaunegommeetunbâtondecolle.

c. Qu'est-cequetuasdanstoncartable?

d. Dansmatrousse,jen'aipasdebâtondecolle.

e. Dansmoncartable,iln'yapasd'agendarose.

f. Dansmatrousse,j'aiuntaille-crayonbleu.

8. Spot the Intruder

Identify the words in each sentence the speaker is NOT saying.

a. Dans ma trousse, il n'y a de j'ai un stylo bleu.

b. Dans ma trousse, j'ai il y a un bâton de colle.

c. Dans ma trousse, il y a une gomme, un taille-crayon vert et une règle.

d. Qu'est-ce que tu as n'as pas dans ta trousse?

e. Qu'est-ce qu'il y a sur dans ton cartable?

f. Dans mon cartable, il n'y a pas d'agenda jaune et vert.

g. Dans mon cartable, il y a un crayon, un livre et un cahier rouge.

THE LANGUAGE GYM

9. Catch it, Swap it

Listen, spot the difference between what you hear and the written text and edit each sentence accordingly.

e.g. Dans <u>mon cartable,</u> j'ai une gomme. | ma trousse

a. Dans mon cartable, j'ai un bâton de colle blanc.

b. Dans ma trousse, il y a un stylo noir.

c. Dans mon cartable, il y a une trousse rose.

d. Dans mon cartable, je n'ai pas d'agenda bleu.

e. Dans ma trousse, il n'y a pas de crayon jaune.

f. Dans mon cartable, il n'y a pas d'agenda gris.

g. Je n'ai pas de cahier rouge.

10. Sentence bingo

Write 4 of the sentences into the grid. You will hear sentences in French in a RANDOM ORDER. Tick all 4 of your sentences to win bingo.

1. Dans mon cartable, il y a une calculatrice rose.

2. Dans mon cartable, j'ai un bâton de colle vert.

3. Dans mon cartable, je n'ai pas d'agenda bleu.

4. Dans mon cartable, j'ai un bâton de colle.

5. Je n'ai pas de cahier rouge.

6. Dans ma trousse, il n'y a pas de crayon jaune.

7. Dans mon cartable, il n'y a pas d'agenda rouge.

8. J'ai un stylo.

9. Je n'ai pas de stylo vert.

10. Dans ma trousse, il y a un stylo noir.

11. Listening Slalom

Listen and pick the equivalent English words from each column.
e.g. J'ai un crayon gris et une gomme.

Listening word order alert!

You will hear: J'ai un crayon (*a pencil*) gris (*grey*), as colours (adjectives) follow the noun in French.

e.g.	**I have**	there is	calculator	but there is a ruler.
a.	In my pencil case	**a grey**	a sharpener	**and a rubber.**
b.	In my schoolbag	I have	**pencil**	and a red folder.
c.	I have a black pen	there isn't	a blue book	in my pencil case.
d.	I don't have	folder but I don't have	a yellow ruler	in my schoolbag.
e.	In my pencil case	and a	I have	and a pink pencil.
f.	I have an orange	a white rubber but	a red exercise book	a glue stick.

🏆 Challenge / Défi

Can you read the sentences in French? You could use a colour/pattern to identify the 3 chunks of each sentence!

75

Unit 6. I can say what's in my schoolbag: READING

1. Sylla-bees
Read and put the syllables in the cells in the correct order.

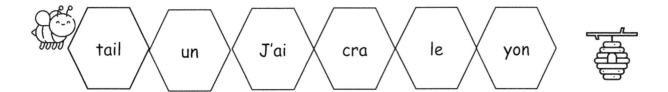

tail | un | J'ai | cra | le | yon

a. *I have a pencil sharpener.*

_____ _____ _____ - _____ .

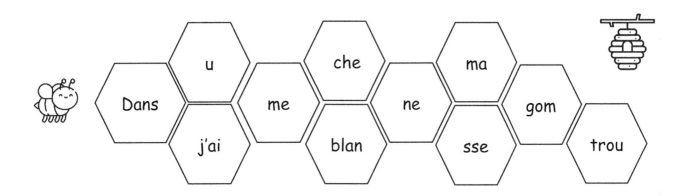

Dans | u / j'ai | me | che / blan | ne | ma / sse | gom | trou

b. *In my pencil case I have a white rubber.*

_____ _____ _____ _____ _____ _____ _____ _____ _____ .

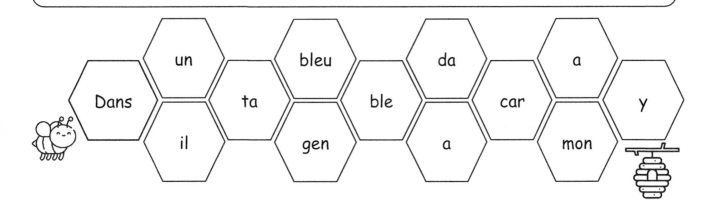

Dans | un / il | ta | bleu / gen | ble | da / a | car | a / mon | y

c. *In my schoolbag there is a blue planner.*

_____ _____ _____ _____ _____ _____ _____ _____ .

2. Read, Match, Find and Colour

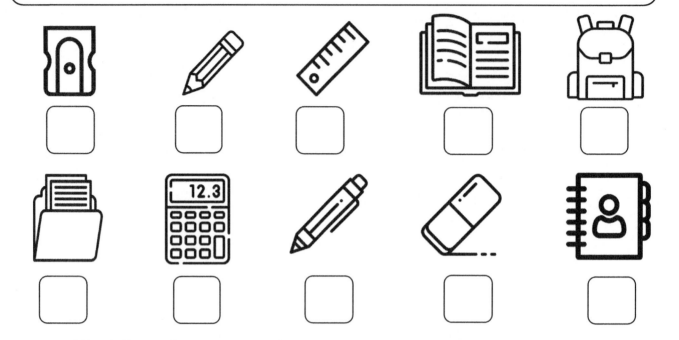

A. Match these sentences to the pictures above.

a. Dans ma trousse, j'ai un crayon gris.

b. J'ai un cartable rouge et noir.

c. Dans ma trousse, il y a une gomme blanche.

d. As-tu une calculatrice?

e. J'ai un stylo vert.

f. Dans mon cartable, il y a un livre vert.

g. J'ai un taille-crayon bleu.

h. Dans ma trousse, il y a une règle rose.

i. Je n'ai pas d'agenda orange.

j. Dans mon cartable, j'ai un classeur.

B. Using the sentences in task A find the French for:

a. a blue pencil sharpener

b. I have a school bag.

c. in my pencil case

d. There is a ruler.

e. a pink ruler

f. I have

g. I have a pen.

h. red and black

i. Do you have...?

j. a green book

THE LANGUAGE GYM

3. True or False
A. Read the paragraphs below and then answer True or False.

Salut! Je m'appelle **Pierre** et j'ai onze ans. Mon anniversaire est le vingt-et-un juillet. J'ai un chat et une tortue. Dans mon cartable, il y a un livre, un classeur rouge et un cahier jaune, mais il n'y a pas de règle.

Salut! Je m'appelle **Amira** et j'ai neuf ans. Mon anniversaire est le trente novembre. J'ai un lapin, mais je n'ai pas de cheval. Dans ma trousse, j'ai un crayon gris, un stylo noir, une gomme orange, mais je n'ai pas de taille-crayon.

	True	False
a. Pierre is 11 years old.		
b. His birthday is the 13th of July.		
c. He has a dog and a cat.		
d. In his schoolbag there is a book.		
e. He has a pink exercise book.		
f. He does not have a ruler.		
g. Amira is 10 years old.		
h. She has a dog but does not have a horse.		
i. In her pencil case she has a blue pen.		
j. She does not have a sharpener.		

B. Find in the texts above the French for:
a. my birthday is

b. in my schoolbag

c. I have a rabbit

d. a red folder

e. I don't have a sharpener

f. an orange rubber

4. Tick or Cross

A. Read the texts. Tick the box if you find the words in the text, cross it if you do not find them.

a. Salut! Je m'appelle **Isa**.

J'ai treize ans. Mon anniversaire est le quinze février. J'ai un poisson qui s'appelle Ricky. Dans mon cartable, il y a une calculatrice, un classeur jaune et un bâton de colle, mais il n'y a pas d'agenda rose.

b. Salut! Je m'appelle **Jean**.

J'ai huit ans. Mon anniversaire est le six juillet. J'ai un lapin, mais je n'ai pas de tortue. Dans ma trousse, j'ai un taille-crayon, un crayon et une règle blanche, mais je n'ai pas de gomme.

	✓	✗
a. J'ai treize ans.		
b. le douze...		
c. dans ma trousse		
d. une calculatrice		
e. un bâton de colle		
f. mais il n'y a pas...		

g. I am 9 years old		
h. the 7th of June		
i. but I don't have...		
j. in my pencil case		
k. a pencil		
l. and a ruler		

B. Find the French in the texts above.

a. the 15th of February _____

b. in my schoolbag _____

c. a yellow folder _____

d. a white ruler _____

e. I do not have a rubber. _____

5. Language detective

- Je m'appelle **Richard**. J'ai dix ans. Mon anniversaire est le cinq mars. J'ai un cheval marron. Dans mon cartable, j'ai un agenda rouge et un livre, mais je n'ai pas de classeur blanc.

- Je m'appelle **Sylvie**. J'ai quatorze ans. Mon anniversaire est le vingt-quatre mai. J'ai un petit chat. Dans ma trousse, j'ai une calculatrice et un cahier vert, mais je n'ai pas de bâton de colle jaune.

- Salut! Je m'appelle **Sandra**. J'ai onze ans. Mon anniversaire est le trente avril. J'ai une grande tortue. Dans mon cartable, il y a une règle jaune et un stylo noir, mais il n'y a pas de taille-crayon gris.

A. Find someone who...

a. ...is 14 years old

b. ...has a red diary

c. ...has a green exercise book

d. ...has a yellow ruler

e. ...does not have a white folder

f. ...has a black pen

g. ...is 10 years old

B. Put a cross in the box and underline the corresponding French translation. One is odd.

and a book	a big tortoise	the 30th of April
a green exercise book	a white horse	I am 11 years old
a grey sharpener	but there isn't	in my school bag
in my pencil case	a yellow glue stick	but I do not have

THE LANGUAGE GYM

Unit 6. I can say what's in my schoolbag: WRITING

1. Spelling

a. u__ __ r__ __ __ __   *a ruler*

b. u__   __ i __ __ __   *a book*

c. __n __ __ __ y __ n   *a pencil*

d. un t__ __ __ __ __ - __ r __ __ __ __   *a pencil sharpener*

e. un __ __ e __ __ __   *a diary*

f. __ n   __ __ __ __ __ a __ __ __   *a schoolbag*

g. __ n b__t__ __ de c__ __ __ __   *a glue stick*

2. Anagrams

a. iJ'a uen rgleè.   *I have a ruler.*

   __'__ __ __ __ __ __ __ __ __ __ __ __.

b. uT sa eun ommge.   *You have a rubber.*

   __ __ __ __ __ __ __ __ __ __ __ __ __ __.

c. eJ ian' spa ed yncroa.   *I don't have a pencil.*

   __ __ __'__ __ __ __ __ __ __ __ __ __ __ __ __ __ __ __.

d. uT sa nu ivrle.   *You have a book.*

   __ __ __ __ __ __ __ __ __ __ __ __.

THE LANGUAGE GYM

3. Gapped Translation

a. J'ai un crayon orange et un bâton de colle.

I have an _____ pencil and a _____.

b. Dans ma trousse, il y a un stylo vert et une règle.

In my pencil case, there is a green _____ and a _____.

c. Je n'ai pas de taille-crayon, mais j'ai une gomme.

I do not have a _____ but I have a _____.

d. Qu'est-ce que tu as dans ton cartable? J'ai un livre.

_____ do you _____ in your _____? I have a _____.

4. Match Up

a. J'ai un taille-

b. Dans mon cartable, il y

c. J'ai une

d. Je n'ai pas

e. Dans ma trousse,

f. Qu'est-ce que tu as

g. Il n'y a pas de stylo

1. j'ai un crayon.

2. crayon bleu.

3. a un livre.

4. dans ta trousse?

5. de cahier vert.

6. noir.

7. trousse rose.

82

5. Rock Climbing

Starting from the bottom, pick one chunk from each row to translate the sentences below.

un agenda rouge.	un classeur.	de règle.	stylo.	gris.
et un crayon	un livre et	j'ai un	mais j'ai	mais je n'ai pas
bâton de colle,	trousse,	une gomme jaune	taille-crayon,	il y a
Dans ma	Je n'ai pas de	Tu as	Dans mon cartable,	J'ai un
a.	b.	c.	d.	e.

a. In my pencil case, I have a pen.

_____

b. I do not have a glue stick but I have a folder.

_____

c. You have a yellow rubber and a grey pencil.

_____

d. In my schoolbag, there is a book and a red diary.

_____

e. I have a sharpener, but I do not have a ruler.

_____

6. Mosaic Translation

Use the words in the grid to help you translate the sentences below.

a.	Dans mon	calculatrice	taille-crayon	J'ai un	gomme rose.
b.	J'ai un	cartable,	noire	et un crayon	trousse.
c.	Dans ma trousse,	tu as	bleu	et une	livre rouge.
d.	Qu'est-ce que	stylo	dans ton cartable?	dans ma	orange.
e.	Il n'y a pas de	j'ai un	il y a un	classeur	vert.

a. In my schoolbag, there is an orange folder.

_____

b. I have a blue pen and a green pencil.

_____

c. In my pencil case, I have a pencil sharpener and a pink rubber.

_____

d. What do you have in your schoolbag? I have a red book.

_____

e. There isn't a black calculator in my pencil case.

_____

7. Sentence Puzzle
Put the words in the correct order.

a. cartable Dans livre j'ai mon un vert

   In my schoolbag, I have a green book.

b. dans ta tu as Qu'est-ce que trousse?

   What do you have in your pencil case?

c. Dans une règle il y a jaune ma trousse

   In my pencil case, there is a yellow ruler.

d. mais un taille-crayon, il n'y a pas de Dans trousse, ma gomme il y a

   In my pencil case, there is a sharpener but there isn't a rubber.

8. Tangled Translation

a. Write the French words in English to complete the translation.

Hello, je m'appelle *Fred.* J'ai *nine years old. My birthday* est le vingt-six *of January. I have* un chien *brown* qui s'appelle Michel. *In my pencil case, there is* une gomme blanche et *a red ruler but* il n'y a pas de *a* taille-crayon *grey*.

b. Write the English words in French to complete the translation.

Bonjour! *My name is* Claire. *I am* treize ans. Mon anniversaire *is the 15ᵗʰ* février. J'ai *a horse* noir qui s'appelle Bandit. ***In my schoolbag, there is*** un livre vert et *a yellow exercise book*, mais il n'y a pas de *pink folder.*

THE LANGUAGE GYM

9. Fill in the gaps

a. Salut! Je m'appelle Jean et _____ onze ans. Mon anniversaire est le _____ juin. Dans ma _____, il y a un _____ , un stylo et _____ gomme _____.

une	crayon	j'ai	vingt	trousse	blanche

b. Salut! _____ m'appelle Caroline. Chez moi, j'ai un _____ gris. Dans mon cartable, _____ un livre, une _____ et un cahier _____, mais il n'y a pas de _____.

taille-crayon	il y a	règle	je	jaune	lapin

10. Guided Translation

a. D____ m__ c_____, i__ y _ u___ a_____ o_____.
In my schoolbag, there is an orange diary.

b. D____ m__ t_____, j'___ u_ c_____ b_____.
In my pencil case, I have a blue pencil.

c. I__ n'__ a p____ d__ g_____ d__ m___ t_____.
There isn't a rubber in my pencil case.

d. J____ n'___ p___ d___ r_____, m____ j'__ u__ l_____.
I don't have a ruler but I have a book.

e. J'___ u___ t_____ r_____ d___ m__ c_____.
I have a red pencil case in my schoolbag.

86

THE LANGUAGE GYM

11. Pyramid Translation
Starting from the top, translate each chunk into French. Write the sentences in the box below.

a. In

b. In my schoolbag, I have...

c. In my schoolbag, I have a yellow book.

d. In my schoolbag, I have a yellow book and a red folder.

e. In my schoolbag, I have a yellow book and a red folder but I don't have a ruler.

a.	
b.	
c.	
d.	
e.	

THE LANGUAGE GYM

12. Staircase Translation

Starting from the top, translate each chunk into French.
Write the sentences in the grid below.

a.	I have	a red pen.				
b.	What	do you have	in your schoolbag?			
c.	In my pencil case,	there is	a green pencil	and a ruler.		
d.	I don't have	a rubber	but	I have	a grey sharpener.	
e.	In my schoolbag,	there isn't	a book	but there is	a calculator	and a diary.

Answers / Réponses

a.	
b.	
c.	
d.	
e.	

Challenge / Défi

Can you create 2 more sentences using the words in the staircase grid above?

☆	
☆	

88

No Snakes No Ladders

7 une tortue verte	6 Je n'ai pas d'animaux.	5 As-tu un animal?	4 dans ma trousse	3 J'ai une règle.	2 J'ai un cheval.	1 J'ai un chat.
8 un mouton blanc	9 Il y a un classeur.	10 Je n'ai pas de pingouin.	11 une souris grise	12 un taille-crayon rouge	13 un grand lapin	14 J'ai une trousse verte.
23 qui s'appelle Doudou	22 J'ai un crayon.	21 J'ai une gomme.	20 un poisson bleu	19 dans mon cartable	18 un chien noir	17 Je n'ai pas de stylo.
24 Il y a un livre bleu.	25 Il n'y a pas de calcula-trice.	26 Il n'y a pas d'agenda blanc.	27 Je n'ai pas de stylo rose.	28 J'ai un cahier orange.	29 un oiseau jaune	30 Tu as une petite araignée.
				15 un cochon d'Inde marron DÉPART	16 Tu as un perroquet.	ARRIVÉE

89

No Snakes No Ladders 2

Unit 5-6

7 a green tortoise	**6** I don't have pets.	**5** Do you have a pet?	**4** in my pencil case	**3** I have a ruler.	**2** I have a horse.	**1** I have a cat.
8 a white sheep	**9** There is a folder.	**10** I don't have a penguin.	**11** a grey mouse	**12** a red pencil sharpener	**13** a big rabbit	**14** I have a green pencil case.
23 who is called Doudou	**22** I have a pencil.	**21** I have a rubber.	**20** a blue fish	**19** in my school bag	**18** a black dog	**17** I don't have a pen.
24 There is a blue book.	**25** There isn't a calculator.	**26** There isn't a white planner.	**27** I don't have a pink pen.	**28** I have an orange exercise book.	**29** a yellow bird	**30** You have a small spider.

DÉPART

15 a brown guinea pig

16 You have a parrot.

ARRIVÉE

90

THE LANGUAGE GYM

UNIT 7
D'OÙ VIENS-TU?

In this unit you will learn how to:

- ✓ Say where you are from
- ✓ Say what languages you speak
- ✓ Use *je viens de / tu viens de*
- ✓ *Use je parle / je ne parle pas, tu parles / tu ne parles pas*
- ✓ Use some connectives

You will revisit:
- ★ Saying your age and birthday
- ★ Talking about your pets

D'où viens-tu?

Je viens de France.

91

THE LANGUAGE GYM

UNIT 7. D'OÙ VIENS-TU?
I can say where I am from and what languages I speak

> D'où viens-tu? *Where are you from?*
> Quelles langues parles-tu? *What languages do you speak?*

Je viens *I am from*	d'Allemagne *Germany*				allemand *German*
	d'Amérique	et *and*	je parle (aussi) *I (also) speak*	un peu *a little*	anglais *English*
	d'Angleterre *England*				
	d'Australie	mais *but*		très bien *very well*	chinois *Chinese*
	de Belgique *Belgium*		je ne parle pas *I don't speak*		espagnol *Spanish*
	de Chine				
	du Canada				français *French*
	d'Écosse *Scotland*				
	d'Espagne *Spain*				gallois *Welsh*
	de France				irlandais *Irish*
	d'Irlande *Ireland*				
	d'Italie *Italy*				italien *Italian*
	du Portugal				portugais *Portuguese*

*Author's note: In French, *'Je viens de'* literally means *'I come from'*, but can also be translated as *'I am from'*, as it is referring to where a person was born.

THE LANGUAGE GYM

Unit 7. Where I am from & languages I speak: LISTENING

1. Split sentences
Listen and match.

a. Je viens d'	1. tu?
b. Je parle	2. de Chine.
c. Je ne viens pas	3. Angleterre.
d. Je ne parle pas	4. Espagne.
e. D'où viens-	5. parles-tu?
f. Je viens d'	6. t'appelles?
g. Quelles langues	7. français.
h. Comment tu	8. espagnol.

2. Faulty Echo

Underline the word which sounds faulty.

e.g. Je viens d'<u>Argentine.</u>

a. Je viens de Chine.

b. Je viens d'Espagne.

c. Je parle allemand.

d. Je viens d'Angleterre.

e. Je parle anglais et français.

f. Je parle italien, mais je ne parle pas portugais.

g. Je parle très bien chinois.

3. Listen and tick the word you hear.

	1	2	3
a.	Angleterre	anglais	français
b.	allemand	chinois	je parle
c.	Espagne	espagnol	je suis
d.	Chine	chinois	je ne suis pas
e.	Italie	je viens de	italien

THE LANGUAGE GYM

4. Fill in the grid with the correct information in English.

		Country	Language
a.	Romain		
b.	Albert		
c.	Patricia		
d.	Raymond		

5. Listen and complete with the missing letters.

a. J_ viens d'Es_agne.

b. Je v_ens de Fran_e.

c. Je p_rle très bi_n anglais.

d. Je ne _arle pas espagno_.

e. Je pa_le aussi all_mand.

f. Parles-t_ chinois? Je p_rle g_llois.

g. Je viens de Ch_ne et je parle f_ançais.

h. Je parl_ français et un peu it_lien.

i. Je viens du Port_gal et je parle p_rtugais.

j. Parles-t_ ital_en? Oui, très bien.

6. Complete with the missing syllables in the box below.

a. Je parle _ _ _nois.

b. Je ne parle pas _ _ _lois.

c. Je viens d'An_ _ _terre.

d. Je parle portu_ _ _ _.

e. Parles-tu _ _glais?

f. Je viens d'É_ _ _se et je parle an_ _ _ _ _.

g. Je viens de _ _ _ _ce et je parle français.

h. Je viens d'Ita_ _ _ et je parle chinois.

i. Je ne parle pas _ _ _ _ bien es_ _gnol.

j. Parles-tu ita_ _ _ _ ? Oui, très bien.

> glais lien Fran gle très an chi pa gais lie gal cos

7. Break the flow: draw a line between words.

a. Jeparleanglaisetaussiitalien.

b. Jeviensd'Allemagne,maisjeparleanglais.

c. JeviensdeChineetjeparleunpeuallemand.

d. Jeneparlepasirlandais,maisjeparleespagnol.

e. Jeparletrèsbienanglaisetfrançais.

f. Quelleslanguesparles-tu?Jeparlechinois.

8. Spot the Intruder

Identify the word(s) in each sentence the speaker is NOT saying.

a. Je parle anglais, espagnol mais je ne viens pas d'Angleterre.

b. Je viens d'Australie et je ne parle pas un peu chinois.

c. Je parle allemand et je parle suis aussi italien.

d. Parles-tu espagnol? Oui, et mais je parle aussi français.

e. Je ne parle pas gallois et mais je parle irlandais.

f. Je viens du Portugal. Je parle portugais italien.

g. Je ne parle pas très bien chinois tu parles.

THE LANGUAGE GYM

9. Catch it, Swap it
Listen, spot the difference between what you hear and the written text and edit each sentence accordingly.

a. Je viens d'Italie et je parle très bien italien et français.

b. Je viens d'Angleterre. Je parle anglais, mais je ne parle pas chinois.

c. Je viens d'Australie. Je parle anglais, mais je ne parle pas espagnol.

d. Je viens d'Amérique et je parle un peu irlandais.

e. Je viens d'Écosse et je parle un peu allemand.

f. Je viens d'Irlande, mais je ne parle pas très bien anglais.

10. Sentence bingo
Write 4 of the sentences into the grid. You will hear sentences in French in a RANDOM ORDER. Tick all 4 of your sentences to win.

1. Je ne parle pas très bien gallois.

2. Je ne parle pas allemand.

3. Je viens d'Irlande.

4. Je parle français, mais je ne parle pas portugais.

5. Je parle anglais, mais je ne parle pas espagnol.

6. Je parle un peu chinois.

7. Je viens d'Angleterre.

8. Je parle très bien portugais.

9. Je viens d'Italie.

10. Je viens d'Australie et je parle très bien italien.

THE LANGUAGE GYM

11. Listening Slalom

Listen in **French** and pick the equivalent English words from each column.

e.g. Je viens de Chine et je parle très bien chinois.

Colour in the boxes for each sentence in a different colour.

e.g.	**I am from**	I am from	but I do not speak	I speak Spanish.
a.	My name is Stéphane.	**China and**	very well	Germany.
b.	Hi!	England	**I speak**	French.
c.	I am	I speak Spanish	Italy but	**Chinese very well.**
d.	I speak	from Spain	but I am from	I speak Portuguese.
e.	You don't speak	a bit of Chinese	and I speak a a bit of	English.
f.	I am not from	Irish	I am from Argentina and	but you speak Italian.

THE LANGUAGE GYM

Unit 7. Where I am from & languages I speak: READING

1. Sylla-Bees

Read and put the syllables in the cells in the correct order.

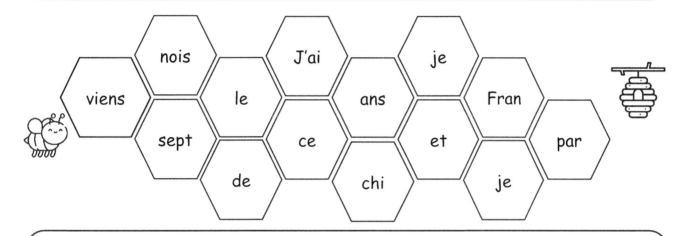

a. *I am seven years old, I am from France and I speak Chinese.*

___ ____ ____ ____,' ___ ____ ____ ___ ____ ___ ___
____ ___ ____ ____.

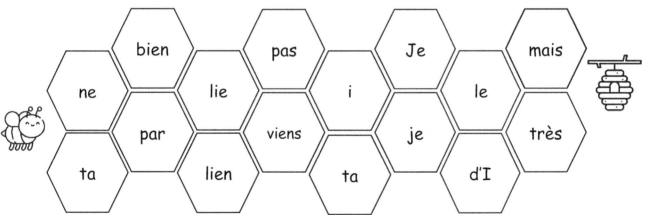

b. *I am from Italy, but I don't speak Italian very well.*

___ ____ ___ ____ ___,' ____ ____ ___ ___ ____ ____
____ ____ ___ ____ ____.

2. True or False
A. Read the paragraphs below and then answer True or False.

Salut! Je m'appelle **Dylan**. J'ai treize ans et j'ai un chien qui s'appelle Pilou. Il a un an et il est très gentil. Je viens d'Espagne et je parle très bien anglais et français. Je parle aussi un peu portugais, mais je ne parle pas allemand. J'aime beaucoup l'espagnol.

Salut! Je m'appelle **Simone**. J'ai douze ans et je n'ai pas d'animaux. Je viens d'Italie et je parle très bien italien et anglais. Je parle aussi un peu français, mais je ne parle pas chinois. J'aime parler espagnol, mais je n'aime pas du tout l'allemand.

	True	False
a. **Dylan** is 13 years old.		
b. He has a little cat.		
c. He comes from Portugal.		
d. He speaks English and French very well.		
e. He doesn't speak German.		
f. He doesn't like Spanish.		
g. **Simone** is French.		
h. She speaks Italian and English a little.		
i. She doesn't speak Chinese.		
j. She doesn't like speaking in Spanish.		

B. Find in the texts above the French for:

a. He is one year old.   b. He is very kind.   c. I do not have pets.

d. I really like...   e. I like to speak...   f. I don't like it at all.

THE LANGUAGE GYM

3. Tick or Cross

A. Read the texts. Tick the box if you find the words in the text, cross it if you do not find them.

- Salut! Je m'appelle **Patricia**.

J'ai neuf ans. Mon anniversaire est le quinze octobre. Je viens d'Australie et je parle très bien anglais et italien. Je parle aussi un peu portugais, mais je ne parle pas chinois. J'aime beaucoup l'allemand.

- Salut! Je m'appelle **Paul**.

J'ai huit ans. Je viens du Canada et je parle très bien anglais et français. Je parle aussi un peu irlandais, mais je ne parle pas italien. Je n'aime pas du tout l'espagnol.

		✓	✗
a.	le quinze mars		
b.	Je viens de France.		
c.	Je ne parle pas...		
d.	Je parle espagnol.		
e.	Je ne parle pas chinois.		
f.	Je n'aime pas....		

g.	I am 6 years old.		
h.	I am from Spain.		
i.	I speak English very well.		
j.	I speak Italian.		
k.	I don't speak...		
l.	I don't like ... at all.		

B. Find the French in the texts above.

a. the 15th of October _____

b. I do not speak Chinese. _____

c. I speak English very well. _____

d. I really like German. _____

e. I do not like Spanish at all. _____

THE LANGUAGE GYM

4. Language Detective

- Je m'appelle **Richard**. <u>J'ai cinq ans.</u> Mon anniversaire est le neuf novembre. Je viens d'Amérique et je parle très bien français et allemand. Je parle aussi un peu portugais, mais je ne parle pas espagnol. Je n'aime pas l'irlandais.

- Je m'appelle **Martine**. J'ai treize ans. Mon anniversaire est le douze mars. J'ai un cheval marron qui s'appelle Artex. Je viens d'Irlande et je parle très bien irlandais et espagnol. Je parle aussi un peu chinois. J'aime l'espagnol.

- Salut! Je m'appelle **Carine**. J'ai onze ans. Mon anniversaire est le vingt juin. Je viens d'Espagne et j'aime l'anglais. Je parle très bien espagnol et allemand. Je parle aussi un peu chinois, mais je ne parle pas français.

A. Find someone who...

a. ...is 13 years old.

b. ...has a brown horse.

c. ...likes English.

d. ...speaks Chinese a little (2).

e. ...speaks French very well.

f. ...speaks German very well (2).

g. ...doesn't speak French.

B. Put a cross in the box and underline the corresponding French translation. One is odd.

I am five years old	I like English	but I don't speak French
I also speak Portuguese a little	the 12th of March	I speak Chinese a little
I am from America	I like Spanish	I don't like Spanish
I don't like Irish	the 20th of June	I am from Spain

THE LANGUAGE GYM

Unit 7. Where I am from & languages I speak: WRITING

1. Spelling

a. a __ __ __ __   a __ __   *German*

b. A __ __ __ ma __ __ __   *Germany*

c. A __ __ __ e __ __ __ r __   *England*

d. a __ __ __ a __ __   *English*

e. J__ p __ __ __ __ e e __ __ __ __ g __ __ __.   *I speak Spanish.*

f. J__ n__ p__ __ l __ p__ __   *I don't speak Chinese.*

c __ __ __ __ __ __.

2. Anagrams

a. eJ rlpae lepsoang.   *I speak Spanish.*

__ __ __ __ __ __ __ __ __ __ __ __ __ __.

b. eJ nvesi d' rrnAetelge.   *I am from England.*

__ __ __ __ __ __ __ __'__ __ __ __ __ __ __ __ __ __.

c. eJ en rlpae spa llmdnaea.   *I don't speak German.*

__ __ __ __ __ __ __ __ __ __ __ __ __ __ __.

d. aiJ'me el gollais.   *I like Welsh.*

__'__ __ __ __ __ __ __ __ __ __ __ __.

e. eJ plrea tuporgsia.   *I speak Portuguese.*

__ __ __ __ __ __ __ __ __ __ __ __ __.

102

THE LANGUAGE GYM

3. Gapped Translation

a. Je parle allemand et français, mais je ne parle pas anglais.

I speak _____ and _____, but I don't speak _____.

b. Je viens d'Allemagne et je parle très bien irlandais.

I am from _____ and I speak Irish _____ _____.

c. Je viens d'Angleterre, mais je ne parle pas anglais.

I am from _____ but I don't speak _____.

d. Quelles langues parles-tu? Je parle irlandais.

What _____ do you _____? I speak _____.

4. Match Up

a. Je parle très

b. Je ne parle

c. Je parle un

d. Je parle un peu

e. Je ne

f. Quelles langues

g. D'où

1. parles-tu?

2. portugais.

3. pas anglais.

4. bien anglais.

5. peu français.

6. parle pas chinois.

7. viens-tu?

a	b	c	d	e	f	g

103

THE LANGUAGE GYM

5. Rock Climbing

Starting from the bottom, pick one chunk from each row to translate the sentences below.

Angleterre.	français.	irlandais.	allemand.	anglais.
Je parle	Je viens d'	et je ne parle pas	et	mais je ne parle pas
chinois,	France	anglais	parles-tu?	viens-tu?
Je viens de	Je parle très bien	Quelles langues	D'où	Je parle un peu
a.	b.	c.	d.	e.

a. I am from France and I don't speak German.

_____

b. I speak Chinese very well, but I don't speak French.

_____

c. What languages do you speak? I speak English.

_____

d. Where are you from? I am from England.

_____

e. I speak a bit of English and Irish.

_____

6. Mosaic Translation

Use the words in the grid to help you translate
the sentences below.

a.	Je viens d'	parles-tu?	français	très bien	chinois.
b.	D'où	Italie	Je viens	et	Angleterre.
c.	Je parle	viens-tu?	mais je parle	d'	allemand.
d.	Quelles langues	un peu	Je parle	aussi	et français.
e.	Je parle très bien	anglais,	et je parle	italien	espagnol.

a. I am from Italy and I speak Italian and French.

_____

b. Where are you from? I am from England.

_____

c. I speak a bit of French and Chinese.

_____

d. What languages do you speak? I speak German very well.

_____

e. I speak English very well, but I also speak Spanish.

_____

105

7. Fill in the Gaps

a. Salut! Je m'appelle Robert. J'ai _____ ans. Mon anniversaire est

le vingt _____. Je viens d' _____ et _____ allemand et

_____. Je parle aussi un _____ anglais.

peu	Italie	huit	juin	français	je parle

b. Salut! Je m'appelle Marie. J'ai un chien _____. Je viens _____

France. Je parle très _____ allemand et espagnol. Je parle

_____ un _____ français. J'aime beaucoup le _____.

portugais	peu	noir	bien	aussi	de

8. Tangled Translation

a. Write the French words in English to complete the translation.

Hello, **je m'appelle** *Michel*. **J'ai** *seven years old. My birthday* **est le treize** *of March*. **Je viens** *from* **France**. *I speak French and English* **très bien. Je** *also* **parle un peu** *Italian*, **mais** *I don't speak* **allemand**.

b. Write the English words in French to complete the translation.

Bonjour! ***My name is*** Lauren. ***I am*** douze ans. Mon anniversaire ***is the 4th*** avril. J'ai ***a dog*** noir ***who is called*** Colli. Je viens d'***Germany***. ***I speak*** très bien anglais ***and*** je parle ***a bit of French***, mais ***I don't speak*** italien.

THE LANGUAGE GYM

9. Sentence Puzzle

Put the words in each sentence in the correct order.

a. très Je parle anglais français et bien.

   I speak English and French very well.

b. Quelles espagnol Je parle langues parles-tu?

   What languages do you speak? I speak Spanish.

c. D' viens-tu? Australie d' Je viens où.

   Where are you from? I am from Australia.

d. anglais, Je parle mais je parle ne pas allemand.

   I speak English, but I don't speak German.

10. Guided Translation

a. S_____! J___ m'_____ C_____. J___ v_____ d'A_____.

Hi! My name is Claire. I am from Australia.

b. J___ v_____ d'E_____. J___ p_____ t_____ b_____ i_____.

I am from Spain. I speak Italian very well.

c. J___ p_____ t_____ b_____ f_____ e ___ j ___ p_____ u___ p_____

i_____.

 I speak French very well and I speak Irish a little.

d. J___ p_____ a_____ et f_____, m_____ j___ n___ p_____

p_____ c_____.

I speak German and French but I don't speak Chinese.

11. Pyramid Translation
Starting from the top, translate each chunk into French. Write the sentences in the box below.

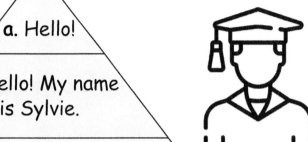

a. Hello!

b. Hello! My name is Sylvie.

c. Hello! My name is Sylvie. I speak German.

d. Hello! My name is Sylvie. I speak German and French.

e. Hello! My name is Sylvie. I speak German and French but I don't speak Chinese.

a.

b.

c.

d.

e.

12. Staircase Translation

Starting from the top, translate each chunk into French.
Write the sentences in the grid below.

a.	I am from	Ireland.				
b.	I speak	English	and French.			
c.	I do not speak	German,	but I speak	Italian.		
d.	I speak	Chinese	very well,	but I do not speak	Spanish.	
e.	I am from	Scotland.	I speak	a little Portuguese	but I don't speak	Irish.

Answers / Réponses

a.	
b.	
c.	
d.	
e.	

🏆 Challenge / Défi

Can you create 2 more sentences using the words in the staircase grid above?

☆	
☆	

UNIT 8

QUEL TEMPS FAIT-IL?

In this unit you will learn how to:

- ✓ Understand and use weather expressions
- ✓ Use time frames and seasons
- ✓ Use *aujourd'hui / il y a / il fait*
- ✓ Find a place on the map

You will revisit:

- ★ Countries and languages
- ★ Names of French locations

Quel temps fait-il aujourd'hui?

Aujourd'hui, il y a du soleil.

110

Unit 8. THE WEATHER
I can describe what the weather is like.

Quel temps fait-il? *What is the weather like?*

En hiver *In winter*	il fait chaud *it is hot*		à Avignon
	il fait froid *it is cold*		à Bordeaux
En automne *In autumn*	il fait beau *it is good weather*		à Brest
Au printemps *In spring*	il fait mauvais *it is bad weather*		à Calais
			à Dieppe
En été *In summer*	il y a du soleil *it is sunny*		à Lille
Cette semaine *This week*	il y a du vent *it is windy*		à Marseille
			à Montpellier
Aujourd'hui *Today*	il y a du brouillard *it is foggy*		à Nice
Normalement *Normally*			à Paris
	il y a des nuages *it is cloudy*		à Poitiers
D'habitude *Usually*	il y a des orages *it is stormy*		à Rouen
	il pleut *it rains*		
	il neige *it snows*		

THE LANGUAGE GYM

Unit 8. What the weather is like: LISTENING

1. Listen and tick the word you hear.

	1	2	3
a.	Il y a du soleil	Il fait froid	Il fait chaud
b.	Il y a des orages	Il y a du vent	Il y a du brouillard
c.	Il neige	Il y a du brouillard	Il pleut
d.	Il fait beau	Il fait mauvais	Quel temps fait-il?
e.	Il y a des orages	Il y a des nuages	Il y a du vent

2. Faulty Echo

Underline the word which sounds faulty.

e.g. <u>Aujourd'hui</u>, il y a du soleil.

a. En hiver, il fait froid.

b. Normalement, il pleut.

c. En été, il fait chaud.

d. Aujourd'hui, il y a des orages.

e. D'habitude, il fait beau.

f. Quel temps fait-il?

g. Cette semaine, il y a du vent.

3. Listen and match.

a. today   1.

b. normally   2.

c. in summer   3.

d. in autumn   4.

e. in winter   5.

f. this week 6.

g. in spring   7.

a	b	c	d	e	f	g

4. Listen and complete with the missing letter.

a. Il fa__t froid.

b. Il __ a du vent.

c. Aujo__rd'hui, il pleut.

d. Il y __ des orages.

e. Il __ait chaud.

f. __l y a du soleil.

g. Aujourd'__ui, il neige.

h. Il fai__ mauvais.

i. I__ y a des nuages.

5. Listen and complete with the missing letters.

a. Au printemps, il pl __ __ __.

b. Aujourd'hui, il fait b__ __ __.

c. En automne, il fait fr__ __ __.

d. En hiver, il __ __ __ge.

e. D'ha__ __tude, il y a du soleil.

f. En été, il fait ch__ __ __.

g. En hiver, il fait __ __ __vais.

bi   aud   oid   eut   mau   nei   eau

6. Break the flow: draw a line between words.

a. Queltempsfait-ilaujourd'hui?Ilneige.

b. Enété,ilfaitchaudàParis.

c. Enautomne,ilfaitbeauàMarseille.

d. Enhiver,ilfaitfroidàCalais.

e. D'habitude,ilyadesnuagesàPoitiers.

f. Aujourd'hui,ilyaduventetilpleutàBrest.

THE LANGUAGE GYM

7. Complete with the missing syllables in the box below.

a. À Dieppe, il fait __ __ __ __.

b. À Marseille, il y a du __ __leil.

c. À Calais, il __ __ __ __ __.

d. À Bordeaux, il fait __ __ __vais.

e. À Lille, il y a des __ __ __ ges.

f. À A__ __gnon, il y a du vent.

g. À Rouen, il __ __ __ge.

h. À Brest, il fait __ __ __ __ __.

i. À Paris, il y a des o__ __ges.

j. À Poitiers, il fait __ __ __ __ __.

| nua | froid | chaud | pleut | nei | beau | ra | mau | so | vi |

8. Fill in the grid with the correct information in English.

	when	weather
a.		
b.		
c.		
d.		
e.		
f.		

9. Spot the Intruder

Identify the word(s) in each sentence the speaker is NOT saying.

a. Quel temps fait-il pas à Lille?

b. À Rouen, il fait il y a beau.

c. À Dieppe, comment il fait mauvais.

d. Aujourd'hui, il y a j'ai des nuages.

e. À Calais, il pleut il y a du vent.

f. En hiver, chaud il pleut à Brest.

THE LANGUAGE GYM

10. Listening Slalom

Listen in French and pick the 3 equivalent English parts from each column.

e.g. Aujourd'hui, il fait chaud à Nice.

You could colour each sentence in a different colour. Then, read the sentence out loud.

e.g.	Today	it is stormy	in Avignon.
a.	Normally	it is hot	in Bordeaux.
b.	In spring	it is bad weather	in Nice.
c.	In autumn	it is cold	in Calais.
d.	Today	it is good weather	in Paris.
e.	Usually	it rains	in Poitiers.
f.	This week	it snows	in Rouen.
g.	Today	it is sunny	in Dieppe.

 THE LANGUAGE GYM

Unit 8. What the weather is like: READING

1. Sylla-Bees

Read and put the syllables in the cells in the correct order.

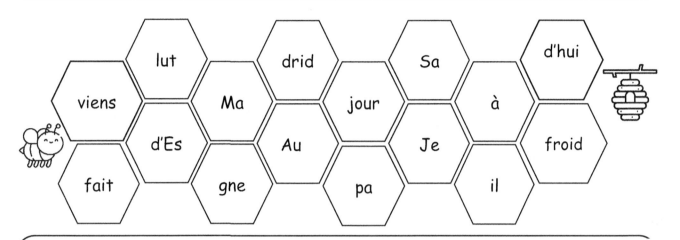

a. *Hi! I am from Spain. Today in Madrid it is cold.*

___ ___! ___ ___ ___ ___ ___. ___ ___ ___, ___
___ ___, ___ ___ ___ ___.

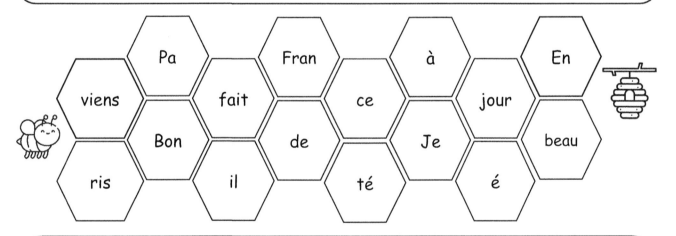

b. *Good morning! I am from France. In summer in Paris it is good weather.*

___ ___! ___ ___ ___ ___ ___. ___ ___ ___, ___
___ ___, ___ ___ ___.

2. True or False?
Look at the map and for each sentence tick True or False.

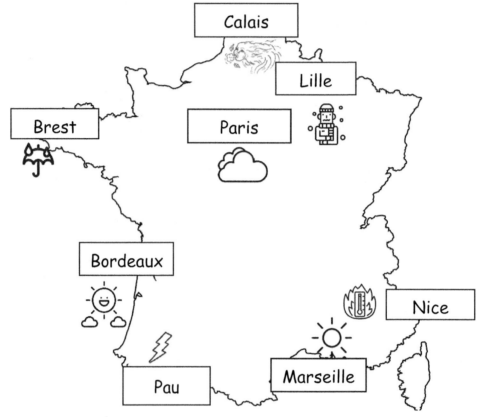

a. Aujourd'hui, à Paris, il fait chaud.

b. Normalement, à Bordeaux, il fait beau.

c. À Nice, il fait froid.

d. Aujourd'hui, à Marseille, il y a du soleil.

e. Cette semaine, à Brest, il neige.

f. Normalement, à Calais, il y a du vent.

g. Aujourd'hui, à Pau, il y a des orages.

h. Cette semaine, il pleut à Lille.

	True	False
a.		
b.		
c.		
d.		
e.		
f.		
g.		
h.		

 **THE LANGUAGE GYM**

3. Read, Match, Find and Colour

A. Match these sentences to the pictures above.

a. Cette semaine, il neige à Paris.

b. Normalement, il y a du soleil à Nice.

c. Aujourd'hui, il y a des orages à Rouen.

d. En hiver, il pleut à Lille.

e. En automne, il y a du vent à Dieppe.

f. Au printemps, il fait beau.

g. D'habitude, il y a des nuages à Brest.

h. En été, il fait chaud à Marseille.

i. Aujourd'hui, il fait mauvais à Poitiers.

j. Cette semaine, il fait froid à Calais.

B. Using the sentences in task A find the French for:

a. It is hot.

b. It is cloudy.

c. in winter

d. It is good weather.

e. this week

f. It is cold.

g. It rains.

h. today

i. It is sunny.

j. It is windy.

THE LANGUAGE GYM

4. True of False?
A. Read the paragraphs below and then answer True or False.

Salut! Je m'appelle **David**. J'ai dix ans. Je viens de France et je parle très bien français. En France, normalement, il fait chaud, mais aujourd'hui, il ne fait pas beau, il fait froid et il pleut.

Salut! Je m'appelle **Paula**. J'ai quatorze ans. Je viens de Belgique et je parle très bien anglais et chinois. En Belgique, d'habitude, il fait mauvais, mais aujourd'hui, il y a du soleil et il fait beau.

	True	False
a. **David** is fourteen years old.		
b. He speaks French very well.		
c. He is from Germany.		
d. It is normally hot in France.		
e. It is not cold today in France.		
f. It is raining in France today.		
g. **Paula** is from France.		
h. In Belgium it is usually bad weather.		
i. She speaks Spanish very well.		
j. It is sunny in Belgium today.		

B. Find in the texts above the French for:

a. ...but today...

b. ...it is normally hot...

c. In Belgium, it is usually bad weather...

d. ...but the weather is not good today...

119

5. Language Detective

- Je m'appelle **Pierre**. Mon anniversaire est le douze décembre. <u>Je viens d'Irlande</u> et je parle anglais et français, mais je ne parle pas chinois. À Dublin, d'habitude, en hiver, il y a des orages, mais aujourd'hui, il fait chaud et il ne pleut pas.

- Je m'appelle **Carine**. Mon anniversaire est le onze décembre. Je viens du Québec et je parle français. Je parle aussi un peu italien. À Montréal, en été, il fait toujours beau, mais aujourd'hui, il y a des nuages et il y a un peu de vent.

- Je m'appelle **Daniel**. J'ai douze ans. Mon anniversaire est le treize décembre. J'habite en Italie. Normalement, à Rome, au printemps, il fait beau, mais aujourd'hui, il pleut et il fait froid. Je n'aime pas quand il fait froid.

A. Read & answer the questions.

a. Who lives in Italy?

b. Who doesn't speak Chinese?

c. Where isn't it raining today?

d. Where is it raining today?

e. Where is the weather usually good?

f. Who speaks a bit of Italian?

g. Where is it cloudy today?

B. Put a cross in the box and underline the corresponding French translation. Two are odd.

I am from Ireland.	I speak English and French.	I have a white and grey cat
I am from England	I don't like when it is cold	I speak a little Italian
....but it rains today	My birthday is the 11th of December	It is a bit windy
...but it is cloudy today	My birthday is the 12th of December	It is hot today

120

1. Spelling

a. a __ p __ __ __ t __ __ __ __   *in spring*

b. e__ h __ v __ __   *in winter*

c. I__ f __ __ t b __ __ u.   *It's good weather.*

d. e __ __ __ __ o __ __ __   *in autumn*

e. I__ __ l __ __ __ .   *It rains.*

f. I__ y __ d__ __ o__ __ __ __ s.   *It's stormy.*

g. I__ y a d__ __ n __ __ __ __ s.   *It's cloudy.*

h. E __ é __ __ , i __ f __ __ __ c __ a __ __. *In summer, it is hot.*

2. Gapped Translation

a. Je viens d'Australie et aujourd'hui il fait beau.

I am _____ Australia and it is _____ weather _____.

b. En automne, il y a du vent à New York.

In _____, it is _____ in New York.

c. Je viens d'Angleterre et d'habitude, il ne fait pas beau.

I ___ from England and _____, it is not _____ weather.

d. Je viens d'Écosse et normalement, il fait mauvais.

I am from _____ and _____, it is _____ weather.

e. Aujourd'hui, il y a des nuages et il y a du vent, mais il n'y a pas d'orages.

Today it is _____ and it is _____, but it isn't _____.

THE LANGUAGE GYM

3. Fill in the gaps

a. Salut! Je m'appelle Claude. J'ai _____ ans. Je viens ___

Angleterre. À Londres, d' _____, il y a du _____ et

_____ froid, _____ aujourd'hui, il fait chaud.

mais	vent	quatorze	d'	habitude	il fait

b. Salut! ___ m'appelle Julia. Je viens d'Italie et _____ dix ans.

_____ Italie, en _____, il fait _____, mais aujourd'hui, il

pleut et il y a des _____.

j'ai	je	été	beau	nuages	en

4. Sentence Puzzle
Put the words in the correct order.

a. Espagne, beau fait il En.

   It is good weather in Spain.

b. Angleterre, En mauvais il fait et pleut il.

   In England, it is bad weather and it rains.

c. Quel fait-il Italie? temps en.

   What is the weather like in Italy?

d. aujourd'hui et du vent, il n'y a pas Il pleut il y a d'orages mais.

   It is raining and it is windy, but it isn't stormy today.

122

No Snakes No Ladders

Unit 7-8

DÉPART	1 Je viens de...	2 Je viens d'Espagne.	3 Je parle espagnol.	4 Je viens d'Angle-terre.	5 Je ne parle pas.	6 Je ne parle pas gallois.	7 Il fait chaud.
15 mais je ne parle pas	14 D'où viens-tu?	13 Je viens de Chine.	12 Aujour-d'hui, il y a du brouillard	11 Il fait froid.	10 Je parle français.	9 en été	8 Quel temps fait-il?
16 Il y a du vent.	17 Il fait beau.	18 en hiver	19 au printemps	20 Quelles langues parles-tu?	21 Je parle anglais.	22 Je viens d'Alle-magne	23 un peu italien
ARRIVÉE	30 Il neige à Lille.	29 Je parle très bien allemand.	28 Il y a du soleil à Nice.	27 Il y a des nuages à Paris.	26 Il pleut à Madrid.	25 cette semaine	24 Il y a des orages.

THE LANGUAGE GYM

No Snakes No Ladders

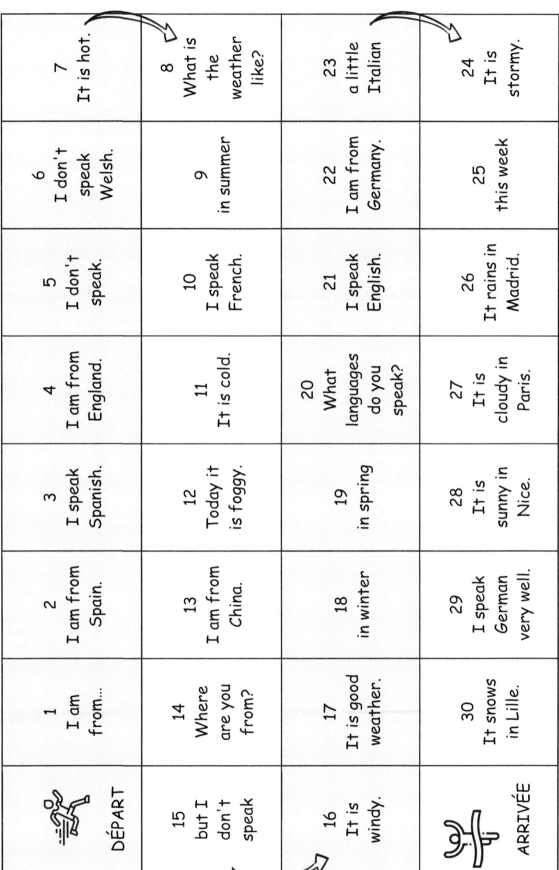

7 It is hot.	6 I don't speak Welsh.	5 I don't speak.	4 I am from England.	3 I speak Spanish.	2 I am from Spain.	1 I am from... **DÉPART**
8 What is the weather like?	9 in summer	10 I speak French.	11 It is cold.	12 Today it is foggy.	13 I am from China.	14 Where are you from?
23 a little Italian	22 I am from Germany.	21 I speak English.	20 What languages do you speak?	19 in spring	18 in winter	17 It is good weather.
24 It is stormy.	25 this week	26 It rains in Madrid.	27 It is cloudy in Paris.	28 It is sunny in Nice.	29 I speak German very well.	30 It snows in Lille. **ARRIVÉE**

15 but I don't speak

16 It is windy.

124

  **THE LANGUAGE GYM**

UNIT 9
OÙ HABITES-TU?

In this unit you will learn how to say in French:

✓ Where you live
✓ Say if you like / dislike where you live and why
✓ Use *j'habite / tu habites*
✓ Use *j'adore / j'aime / je n'aime pas / je déteste*

You will revisit:
★ Masculine/ feminine adjectival agreement
★ Word order noun + adjective

J'habite à Paris.

J'adore ma ville car elle est jolie.

THE LANGUAGE GYM

Où habites-tu? *Where do you live?*
Aimes-tu ta ville? *Do you like your town?*

J'habite à *I live in*	Bordeaux Bruges Bruxelles Dieppe Édimbourg *Edinburgh* Gatineau Harrogate Londres *London* Marseille Montréal New York Rennes Rome	J'adore *I love* J'aime *I like* Je n'aime pas *I don't like* Je déteste *I hate*	mon village *my village*	car il est *because it is* car il n'est pas *because it is not*	animé *lively* bruyant *noisy* calme *quiet* grand *big* joli *pretty* moche *ugly* petit *small* touristique *touristy*
			ma ville *my town*	car elle est *because it is* car elle n'est pas *because it is not*	animée *lively* bruyante *noisy* calme *quiet* grande *big* jolie *pretty* moche *ugly* petite *small* touristique *touristy*

126

Unit 9: Where I live: LISTENING

1. Listen and tick the word you hear. ✓

	1	2	3
a.	Londres	j'habite	village
b.	j'aime	ville	joli
c.	jolie	village	je déteste
d.	animée	bruyante	grande
e.	j'adore	calme	j'habite

2. Faulty Echo

Underline the word which sounds faulty.

e.g. J'habite à Dieppe.

a. J'aime mon village.

b. J'adore ma ville.

c. Je n'aime pas ma ville.

d. J'habite à Londres.

e. Mon village est petit.

f. Ma ville est moche.

g. ...car elle est bruyante.

h. ...car il est calme.

3. Listen and complete with the missing letters.

a. J'hab___te à New York.

b. Ma v___lle est j___lie.

c. Mon vill___ge est p___tit.

d. J'h___bite ___ Édimbourg.

e. M___ ville est c___lme.

f. Mon v___llage est j___li.

g. M___n village est br___yant.

h. J'aim___ ma vill___.

i. Je n'aime p___s mon v___llage.

j. Ma ville est p___tit___.

THE LANGUAGE GYM

4. Narrow Listening: gap-fill

a. Salut! Je m'appelle Fabien et j'ai onze ____. Je viens d' _____, mais

j'habite ____ Angleterre. Je parle un _____ anglais et je parle très

_____ irlandais et _____. J'aime mon _____

car il est calme et _____.

espagnol	en	bien	Irlande	village	ans	peu	joli

b. Salut! Je m'appelle Rose et j'ai _____ ans. Je viens ____ Espagne, mais

_____ en Allemagne. Je parle_____, espagnol et_____.

J'adore ma _____ car elle ____ grande mais _____.

j'habite	allemand	onze	ville	bruyante	est	d'	français

5. Fill in the grid with the correct information in English.

		🙂 Opinion 🙁	Reason (Adjective)
a.	Albert		
b.	Antoine		
c.	Lorène		
d.	Charlotte		
e.	Michel		
f.	Franck		

THE LANGUAGE GYM

6. Complete with the missing syllables in the box below.

a. __ ' __ __ bite à Madrid.

b. Ma ville est mo __ __ __.

c. J'ai__ __ ma ville.

d. Je dé__ __ __te ma ville.

e. J'adore mon __ __ __lage.

f. Je n'aime __ __ __ mon village.

g. J'aime __ __ __ village.

h. Mon village est __ __ che.

i. Ai__ __ __ -tu ton village?

j. Mon village est bru__ __ __ __.

vil	mo	yant	mon	tes	pas	j'ha	mes	me	che

* Author's note: Ask your teacher how many syllables there are in *"bruyant"* – officially there is only one, but many French speakers say there are two. ☺

7. Spot the Intruder

Identify the word in each sentence the speaker is NOT saying.

a. J'habite à Londres. J'aime ma ville car elle est pas jolie.

b. J'habite à Domme. Je n'aime pas mon le village car il est petit.

c. J'habite à Rome et je déteste ma ville car elle est très bruyante.

d. J'adore ma ville car elle est grande, jolie et animée.

e. Je n'aime pas la ma ville car elle est calme.

f. J'habite à en New York. J'adore ma ville car elle est grande.

g. J'aime mon village car où il est touristique.

h. Mon je n'aime pas ma ville car elle est moche.

129

 **THE LANGUAGE GYM**

8. Catch it, Swap it

Listen, spot the difference between what you hear and **the written** text and edit each sentence accordingly.

e.g. J'aime ma ville car elle est <u>jolie</u>.

calme

a. Je n'aime pas mon village car il est petit.

b. Je déteste ma ville car elle est très grande.

c. J'adore ma ville car elle est calme.

d. Je n'aime pas ma ville car elle est bruyante.

e. Je n'aime pas ma ville car elle est moche.

f. J'aime mon village car il est calme.

g. J'adore New York car c'est une ville animée.

9. Sentence bingo

Write 4 of the sentences into the grid. You will hear sentences in French in a RANDOM ORDER. Tick all 4 of your sentences to win!

1. Je n'aime pas mon village car il est petit.

2. Je n'aime pas mon village car il est moche.

3. J'aime mon village car il est calme.

4. J'adore ma ville car elle est calme.

5. Je déteste ma ville car elle est très grande.

6. J'aime ma ville car elle est jolie.

7. Je n'aime pas ma ville car elle est horrible.

8. J'aime ma ville car elle est grande.

9. Je déteste ma ville car elle est moche.

10. J'adore New York car c'est une ville animée.

THE LANGUAGE GYM

10. Listening Slalom

Listen in French and pick the equivalent English words from each column.

e.g. Je m'appelle Jean, j'habite à Madrid. J'adore ma ville.

Colour in the boxes for each sentence in a different colour.

e.g.	My name is Jean	because it is pretty	lively and touristy.
a.	I live in New York	**I live in Madrid**	and quiet.
b.	I live in Marseille	I love my town	**I love my town.**
c.	I don't like	It is big	because it is lively.
d.	I like my town	I like my town	and big.
e.	I hate my town	my town because	because it is touristy.
f.	I live in London	because it is ugly	it is small.

Unit 9: Where I live: READING

1. Read and put the syllables in the cells in the correct order.

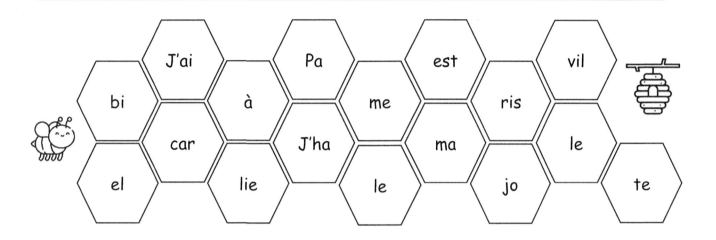

a. *I live in Paris. I like my town because it is pretty.*

____ ____ ____ ____ ____ ____. ____ ____ ____ ____ ____

____ ____ ____ ____ ____ ____ ____.

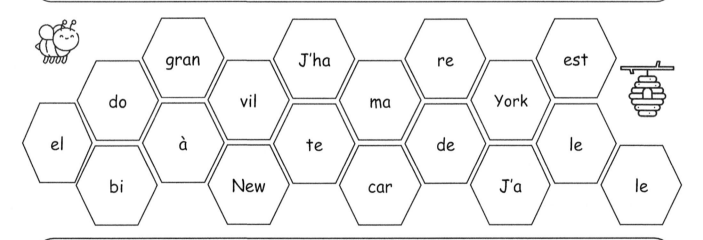

b. *I live in New York. I love my town because it is big.*

____ ____ ____ ____ ____ ____ ____. ____ ____ ____ ____ ____

____ ____ ____ ____ ____ ____ ____.

THE LANGUAGE GYM

2. True or False

A. Read the paragraphs below and then answer True or False.

Salut! Je m'appelle **Paul**. J'ai cinq ans. Je viens de France et je parle très bien anglais. En France, normalement, il fait chaud. J'habite à Paris. J'aime ma ville car elle est grande et touristique.

Salut! Je m'appelle **Annie**. J'ai onze ans. Je viens d'Allemagne et je parle allemand et français. En Allemagne, d'habitude, il fait froid. J'habite à Bibury, en Angleterre. J'adore mon village car il est petit et joli. Il est aussi touristique.

	True	False
a. **Paul** is 15 years old.		
b. He speaks French very well.		
c. He lives in Paris.		
d. It is normally cold in France.		
e. He likes his town.		
f. His town is big and lively.		
g. **Annie** is from Germany.		
h. It is usually cold in Germany.		
i. She lives in Germany.		
j. She likes her village because it is quiet.		

B. Find in the texts above the French for:

a. It is normally hot.   b. It is small and pretty.   c. I love

d. It is usually cold.   e. It is big and touristy.   f. I live in Paris.

THE LANGUAGE GYM

3. Tick or Cross

A. Read the texts. Tick the box if you find the words in the text, cross it if you do not find them.

Salut! Je m'appelle **Patricia**.
J'ai dix ans. Je viens du Québec et je parle très bien français et allemand. J'habite à Gatineau. Aujourd'hui, il pleut à Gatineau. J'aime ma ville car elle est animée, mais elle est bruyante.

Salut! Je m'appelle **Lou**.
J'ai sept ans. Je viens de France et je parle très bien français, mais je ne parle pas italien. J'habite à Paris. Normalement, à Paris, il y a du soleil. Je déteste ma ville car elle est touristique et bruyante. Je préfère une ville calme.

	✓	✗
a. J'ai dix ans.		
b. Je viens du Québec.		
c. je parle un peu		
d. J'habite à Paris.		
e. je n'aime pas		
f. Elle est animée.		

	✓	✗
g. I am 6 years old.		
h. I am from Spain.		
i. I hate my town.		
j. I don't speak French.		
k. it's sunny		
l. because it is noisy		
m. a quiet town		

B. Find the French in the texts above.

a. Today in Gatineau, it is raining. _____

b. I prefer a quiet town. _____

c. In Paris, it is normally sunny. _____

d. I hate my town because it is touristy. _____

e. ...because it is lively, but it is noisy. _____

THE LANGUAGE GYM

4. Language Detective

- Je m'appelle **Richard**. Mon anniversaire est le trois décembre. Je n'ai pas d'animaux. <u>Je viens d'Irlande,</u> mais j'habite à Londres en Angleterre. J'aime ma ville car elle est animée et touristique, mais normalement, il fait mauvais.

- Je m'appelle **Aurélie**. J'ai treize ans. J'ai un chien blanc et noir qui s'appelle Fifi. Je viens de Belgique et j'habite à Bruges. J'aime ma ville car elle est calme et jolie. D'habitude, il fait aussi beau.

- Salut! Je m'appelle **Danielle**. J'ai onze ans. J'ai un chat blanc et gris qui s'appelle Jupiter. Je viens de France, mais j'habite au Canada à Montréal. Je n'aime pas ma ville car elle est moche et bruyante. Aujourd'hui, il pleut à Montréal.

A. Find someone who...

a. ...is 11 years old.

b. ...has a black and white dog.

c. ...lives in a town.

d. ...has a white and grey cat.

e. ...lives in an ugly and noisy place.

f. ...lives in a lively place.

g. ...doesn't own a cat.

B. Put a cross in the box and underline the corresponding French translation. One is odd.

~~I am from Ireland.~~	...but I live in Canada.	I have a white and grey cat.
I don't have any pets.	I like my town.	I have a white and black dog.
...because it is quiet and pretty	today	It is raining in Montreal today.
...because it is ugly and noisy	I don't like my town.	It is windy.

Unit 9: Where I live: WRITING

1. Spelling

a. a __ __ __ é __   *lively (f)*

b. b __ __ __ __ __ n __   *noisy (m)*

c. d__ __ __   __ __ __   v __ __ l __   *in my town*

d. m__ __   v __ __ __ __ __ __ __   *my village*

e. p __ __ __ __ __   *small (m)*

f. M __ v __ __ __ __ __   e __ __   mo __ __ __.   *My town is ugly.*

g. J'h __ __ __ __ __ __   e à L __ __ __ __   r __ __.   *I live in London.*

2. Anagrams

a. htJ'aebi ne eBqligeu.   *I live in Belgium.*

__'__ __ __ __ __ __ __   __ __   __ __ __ __ __ __ __.

b. aemJ'i dresLon.   *I like London.*

__'__ __ __ __ __   __ __ __ __ __ __ __.

c. eJ étsdete am lleiv.   *I hate my town.*

__ __   __ __ __ __ __ __ __ __   __ __   __ __ __ __ __.

d. rac li ets namié   *because it is lively*

__ __ __ __   __ __   __ __ __   __ __ __ __ __

136

THE LANGUAGE GYM

3. Gapped Translation

a. Je viens d'Australie, mais j'habite en Écosse.

I am _____ Australia but I _____ in Scotland.

b. J'aime mon village car il est très joli et grand.

I like my _____ because it is _____ pretty and _____.

c. J'habite à Londres. J'adore ma ville.

I _____ in London. I _____ my _____.

d. Aimes-tu ta ville? Non, je n'aime pas ma ville.

Do you like _____ town? No, I don't like _____ town.

e. Où habites-tu? J'habite dans un village animé mais petit.

Where do _____ _____? I live in a _____ but _____ village.

4. Match Up

a. J'habite en

b. Je ne parle pas

c. Je viens

d. J'aime

e. ...car

f. ...car elle est

g. J'adore mon

1. elle est jolie

2. village.

3. ma ville.

4. d'Espagne.

5. touristique

6. français.

7. France.

a	b	c	d	e	f	g

5. Rock Climbing
Starting from the bottom, pick one chunk from each row to translate the sentences below.

elle est petite.	à Rome.	moche.	il est grand.	à Édimbourg.
J'habite	Non, car	et j'habite	car elle est	car
ma ville	Angleterre	ta ville?	mon village	habites-tu?
Je viens d'	Je n'aime pas	Aimes-tu	J'aime	Où
a.	b.	c.	d.	e.

a. I am from England and I live in Rome.

_____

b. I don't like my town because it is ugly.

_____

c. Do you like your town? No, because it is small.

_____

d. I like my village because it is big.

_____

e. Where do you live? I live in Edinburgh.

_____

6. Mosaic Translation

Use the words in the grid to help you translate the sentences below.

a.	Ma ville	est jolie	et joli.	j'adore	petit.
b.	Où	ta ville?	et petite,	Il est aussi	village.
c.	Je n'aime pas	habites-tu?	Oui,	mais elle est	touristique.
d.	Aimes-tu	ma ville	J'habite dans	un grand	bruyante.
e.	Mon village	est calme	car elle est	moche et	Londres.

a. My town is pretty and small, but it is touristy.

_____

b. Where do you live? I live in a big village.

_____

c. I don't like my town because it is ugly and noisy.

_____

d. Do you like your town? Yes, I love London.

_____

e. My village is quiet and pretty. It is also small.

_____

THE LANGUAGE GYM

7. Fill in the gaps

a. Salut! Je m'appelle Simon. J'ai _____ ans. Je viens du _____, mais j'habite ____ Angleterre. _____ un peu allemand. J'aime mon _____ car il ____ calme.

en	je parle	douze	est	village	Québec

b. Salut! Je m'appelle Julia. Je viens d'Italie, mais j'_____ à _____. Je parle très _____ anglais et italien. Je parle aussi un ____ espagnol. J'adore ma _____ car elle est calme ____ jolie.

ville	et	habite	bien	Glasgow	peu

8. Tangled Translation

a. Write the French words in English to complete the translation.

Hello, je m'appelle *Bertrand*. **Je viens du** *Canada*, **mais** *I live* **en Allemagne.** *I speak German* **et français.** *In Germany*, **d'habitude**, *it rains*. *I live* **à Berlin et** *I don't like my town* **car elle est** *very big and* **bruyante.**

b. Write the English words in French to complete the translation.

Bonjour! *My name is* Joe. J'ai *eleven* ans et *I don't have* d'animaux. J'habite *in New York*. J'aime *my town* car elle est *very big* et *pretty*. J'adore *also* ma ville *because* elle est animée et *it is not* moche. À New York, *normally*, il fait beau *and* il fait *hot*.

140

THE LANGUAGE GYM

9. Sentence Puzzle

Put the words in the correct order.

a. jolie ma ville très est J'aime car elle.

I like my town because it is very pretty.

b. Où J'habite Paris à n'aime pas je et habites-tu? ma ville

Where do you live? I live in Paris and I don't like my town.

c. Aimes-tu J'adore il est petit car ton village? mon village

Do you like your village? I love my village because it is small.

d. ma ville bruyante elle est car très Je déteste touristique et aussi.

I hate my town because it is very noisy and also touristy.

10. Guided Translation

a. S_____! J__ m'_____ P_____. J'_____ à R_____.

Hi! My name is Patricia. I live in Rome.

b. J__ v_____ de F_____. J__ p_____ t____ b_____ f_____.

I am from France. I speak French very well.

c. J'_____ d__ u__ v_____. J'_____ m__ v_____ c__ e__ e__ c_____.

I live in a town. I like my town because it is quiet.

d. M__ v_____ e__ a_____ e__ a_____ t_____.

My town is lively and also touristy.

e. O__ h_____ - t__? J'_____ à B_____.

Where do you live? I live in Bordeaux.

THE LANGUAGE GYM

11. Pyramid Translation
Starting from the top, translate each chunk into French. Write the sentences in the box below.

a. Hello!

b. Hello! My name is Charlotte.

c. Hello! My name is Charlotte. I live in London.

d. Hello! My name is Charlotte. I live in London. I like my town because it is big and pretty.

e. Hello! My name is Charlotte. I live in London. I like my town because it is big and pretty, but it is not touristy.

a.
b.
c.
d.
e.

142

THE LANGUAGE GYM

12. Staircase Translation
Starting from the top, translate each chunk into French.
Write the sentences in the grid below.

a.	I like	my town.				
b.	I don't like	my town because	it is touristy.			
c.	I love	my town because	it is pretty	and lively.		
d.	I hate	my town because	it is big,	touristy	and also noisy.	
e.	I like	my town because	it is pretty,	small	and also	quiet.

Answers / Réponses

a.	
b.	
c.	
d.	
e.	

🏆 Challenge / Défi
Can you create 2 more sentences using the words in the staircase grid above?

☆	
☆	

THE LANGUAGE GYM

UNIT 10
DANS MA VILLE

In this unit you will learn how to:

- Say what's in your town
- Practise singular and plural nouns

You will revisit:

★ How to use *il y a / il n'y a pas de*

★ *Un / une*

★ Saying where you live

★ Giving your opinion on your town

Dans mon quartier, il y a une piscine.

Dans ma ville, il y a des restaurants.

144

Unit 10. I can say what's in my town

Qu'est-ce qu'il y a dans ta ville? *What's in your town?*

Dans ma ville *In my town* **Dans mon village** *In my village* **Dans mon quartier** *In my neighbour-hood*	**il y a** *there is*	un centre sportif *a sports centre* un château *a castle* un cinéma *a cinema* un magasin *a shop* un musée *a museum* un parc *a park* un restaurant un stade *a stadium* un supermarché *a supermarket* un temple un théâtre *a theatre*	**et** *and* **et aussi** *and also*	des centres sportifs sports centres des châteaux *castles* des cinémas *cinemas* des magasins shops des musées museums des parcs parks des restaurants des stades stadiums des supermarchés supermarkets des temples des théâtres *theatres*
	il n'y a pas de *there isn't* (*don't use "un", "une" or "des"*)	une bibliothèque *a library* une boulangerie *a bakery* une cathédrale une école *a school* une église *a church* une gare *a train station* une mosquée *a mosque* une pharmacie une piscine *a swimming pool* une place *a square* une plage *a beach*	**or ou**	des bibliothèques *libraries* des boulangeries bakeries des cathédrales des écoles schools des églises churches des gares *train stations* des mosquées *mosques* des pharmacies des piscines *swimming pools* des places squares des plages *beaches*

145

Unit 10. I can say what's in my town: LISTENING

1. Listen and tick the word you hear.

	1	2	3
a.	piscine	place	gare
b.	cinéma	ville	école
c.	il y a	il n'y a pas de	aussi
d.	magasin	théâtre	piscine
e.	stades	églises	dans mon village

2. Faulty Echo

Underline the word which sounds faulty.

e.g. Dans mon <u>village,</u> il y a un cinéma.

a. Dans ma ville, il y a une église.

b. Dans mon village, il y a une bibliothèque.

c. Dans ma ville, il y a des restaurants et des parcs.

d. Dans mon village, il n'y a pas de piscine.

e. Dans ma ville, il y a une place mais il n'y a pas de musée.

f. Dans mon village, il y a un centre sportif et un château.

THE LANGUAGE GYM

3. Listen and complete with the missing vowels.

a. mon vill__ge

b. une pl__ce

c. une pisc__ne

d. ma v__lle

e. un ciném__

f. un m__sée

g. un c__ntre sp__rtif

h. une boulang__rie

i. une égl__se

j. Il y __ une place.

a
e
i
o
u

4. Complete with the missing syllables in the box below.

a. un super __ __ __ ché

b. une __ __ __ langerie

c. un maga __ __ __

d. des é __ __ les

e. une pla __ __

f. une pharma __ __ __

g. une biblio __ __ __ que

h. un __ __ __teau

i. des res __ __ __ rants

j. __ __ ville

co cie bou châ ge mar thè ma sin tau

5. Fill in the grid with the information in English.

	There is (il y a) ✓	*There isn't* (il n'y a pas) ✗
e.g.	a castle	a river
a.		
b.		
c.		
d.		

6. Spot the Intruder

Identify the word(s) in each sentence the speaker is NOT saying.

e.g. Dans mon quartier, il y a une piscine, _église_ et un centre sportif.

a. Dans mon village, il y a des restaurants et un des écoles.

b. J'aime ma ville car il n'y a pas de piscine et une de bibliothèque.

c. J'habite à Londres. Dans ma ville, il y a des musées et aussi des théâtres.

d. J'habite dans un petit village. Il y a des magasins mais il n'y a pas de cinéma.

e. Dans mon village, il y a une pharmacie et j'habite une gare.

f. Qu'est-ce qu'il y a dans ta ville? Il y a une jolie grande plage.

7. Narrow Listening: gap-fill

a. J'habite ____ une _____ ville en France. Dans ma _____, il y a

un _____, une _____ et des _____. J'aime

____ ville car elle est _____ et jolie.

cinéma	ma	grande	piscine	ville	calme	dans	restaurants

b. Je viens d'_____, mais j'habite en _____, dans un

petit _____. J' _____ mon village car il est

_____, mais ____ peu _____.

animé	Allemagne	village	adore	bruyant	un	Espagne

148

8. Listening Slalom

Listen in French and pick the equivalent English words from each column.

e.g. Dans ma ville, il y a un cinéma.

Colour in the boxes for each sentence in a different colour.

e.g.	**In my town**	because it is big.	a swimming-pool.
a.	In my town there is	**there is**	There are restaurants and shops.
b.	I live in Dieppe.	a sports centre	**a cinema.**
c.	In my town there are	a cinema,	and a castle.
d.	I love my neighbourhood	There is a beach	and a museum.
e.	I like my town because	shops, but there isn't	square, but there isn't a stadium.
f.	In my town there isn't	it is pretty. There is a	but there is a library.

THE LANGUAGE GYM

Unit 10. I can say what's in my town: READING

1. Read and put the syllables in the cells in the correct order.

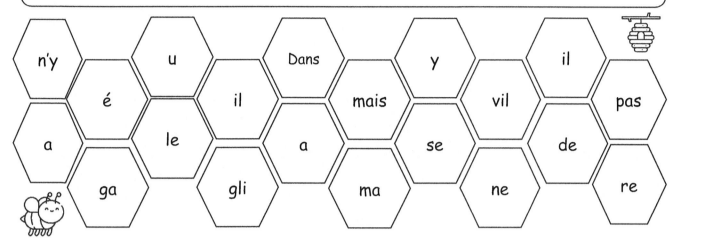

a. *In my town there is a church, but there isn't a train station.*

___ ___ ___ ___ ___ ___, ___ ___ ___ ___ ___ ___ ___ ___,

___ ___ ___ ___ ___ ___ ___ ___ ___.

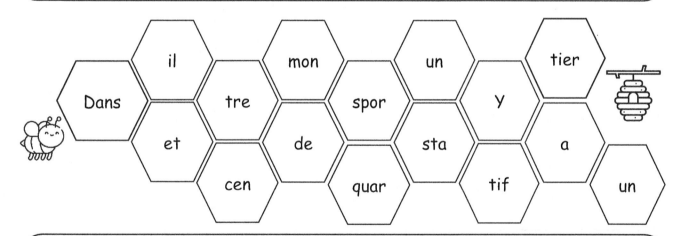

b. *In my neighbourhood there is a sports centre and a stadium.*

___ ___ ___ ___ ___, ___ ___ ___ ___ ___ ___ ___

___ ___ ___ ___ ___ ___.

2. True or false
A. Read the paragraphs below and then answer True or False.

Salut! Je m'appelle **Nicolas**. J'ai quatorze ans. J'habite à Berlin, la capitale de l'Allemagne. J'aime ma ville car elle est grande et touristique, mais elle est bruyante. Dans mon quartier, il y a une bibliothèque, un stade et un centre commercial, mais il n'y a pas de cinéma.

Salut! Je m'appelle **Houda**. Je viens de France, mais j'habite en Espagne. À Madrid, la capitale de l'Espagne, normalement, il fait chaud en été. J'aime ma ville car elle est touristique et jolie. Dans mon quartier, il y a une gare, une mosquée et un parc, mais il n'y a pas de stade.

	True	False
a. **Nicolas** is 14 years old.		
b. He doesn't like his town.		
c. His town is small and touristy.		
d. In his neighbourhood, there is a stadium.		
e. In his neighbourhood, there is a cinema.		
f. **Houda** is from Spain.		
g. She lives in France.		
h. In Madrid, it is normally cold in summer.		
i. In her neighbourhood, there is a train station.		
j. In her neighbourhood, there isn't a stadium.		

B. Find in the texts above the French for:
a. The capital of Germany.

b. There is a train station.

c. I like my town.

d. There isn't a cinema.

THE LANGUAGE GYM

3. Tick or Cross

A. Read the texts. Tick the box if you find the words in the text, cross it if you do not find them.

- Salut! Je m'appelle **Gisèle**.

J'ai sept ans. Je viens de France et j'habite dans un petit village qui s'appelle Giverny. Dans mon village, il y a un château, un musée et une église, mais il n'y a pas de gare.

- Salut! Je m'appelle **Ramón**.

J'ai six ans. Je viens d'Italie et j'habite dans une ville qui s'appelle Rome. J'aime ma ville car elle est belle. Dans mon quartier, il y a un parc, une bibliothèque et une piscine, mais il n'y a pas de cinéma.

	✓	✗
a. J'ai sept ans.		
b. Je viens d'Espagne.		
c. un grand village		
d. Il y a un château.		
e. Il n'y a pas d'église.		
f. qui s'appelle		

g. I am 7 years old.		
h. I am from Italy.		
i. because it is big		
j. in my neighbourhood		
k. a swimming pool		
l. There isn't a park.		

B. Find the French in the texts above.

a. a small village called _____

b. There isn't a train station. _____

c. I live in a town called Rome. _____

d. In my neighbourhood, there is a park. _____

e. ...but there isn't a cinema _____

4. Language Detective

- Je m'appelle **Mario**. J'ai douze ans. Je viens du Portugal, mais j'habite à Paris, la capitale de la France. À Paris, normalement, il fait beau. J'aime ma ville car il y a des parcs, des temples, des cathédrales et le stade 'Paris Saint-Germain' (PSG).

- Je m'appelle **Roberto**. J'ai treize ans. <u>Je viens d'Italie,</u> mais j'habite à Bruxelles, la capitale de la Belgique. À Bruxelles, en été, il fait chaud. J'adore ma ville car elle est touristique. Il y a aussi des musées et l'Atomium.

- Salut! Je m'appelle **Fatima**. J'ai onze ans. Je viens d'Écosse, mais j'habite à Londres, la capitale de l'Angleterre. À Londres, normalement, il pleut. J'aime ma ville car il y a des magasins et des mosquées, mais c'est une ville très bruyante.

A. Find someone who...

a. ...is 13 years old.

b. ...lives in England.

c. ...lives in a town with museums.

d. ...doesn't mention a stadium. (2)

e. ...lives in a town with parks.

f. ...lives in a very noisy town.

g. ...is from Scotland.

B. Put a cross in the box and underline the corresponding French translation. Two are odd.

I am from Italy. ✗	There are parks.	It usually rains in London.
I love my town because it is touristy.	the stadium of PSG	In summer, it is hot in Brussels.
...but I live in England.	...but I live in London	The weather is normally good in Paris.
There are also museums.	I don't like my town.	It's a very noisy town.

Unit 10. I can say what's in my town: WRITING

1. Spelling

a. u __ __ g __ __ __   *a train station*

b. u __ s __ __ d __   *a stadium*

c. u __ __ p __ __ __ __ __ __   *a swimming pool*

d. u __ r __ __ __ __ __ u __ __ __ t   *a restaurant*

e. u __ __ b __ b __ __ __ __ t __ __ __ __ __   *a library*

f. u __ c __ n __ __ __ __ s __ __ __ __ __ i __   *a sports centre*

g. I __ y __ u __ m __ __ é __ .   *There is a museum.*

h. I__ n' __ a p __ __ __ d__ p __ __ __ __ .   *There isn't a park.*

2. Anagrams

a. lI y a nu crpa.   *There is a park.*

__ __ __ __ __ __ __ __ __ __ .

b. lI y a neu théredalca.   *There is a cathedral.*

__ __ __ __ __ __ __ __ __ __ __ __ __ __ __ __ __ __ .

c. lI yn' a spa ed rgae.   *There isn't a train station.*

__ __ __ __'__ __ __ __ __ __ __ __ __ __ __ __ .

d. lI y a sde reutstarans.   *There are restaurants.*

__ __ __ __ __ __ __ __ __ __ __ __ __ __ __ __ __ __ __ .

THE LANGUAGE GYM

3. Gapped Translation

a. Dans mon quartier, il y a un centre sportif et un stade.

In my _____, there is a _____ _____ and a stadium.

b. Dans ma ville, il y a une grande place.

In my _____, there is a big _____.

c. J'habite à Londres. À Londres, il y a des mosquées et un château.

I _____ in London. In London, _____ are mosques and a _____.

d. Qu'est-ce qu'il y a dans ton quartier? Il y a une jolie place.

What ____ there in your neighbourhood? There is a pretty _____.

e. Dans ma ville, il y a une église et une bibliothèque.

In my _____, there is a _____ and a _____.

4. Match Up

a. Il y a   1. ville

b. dans ma   2. mon village

c. dans   3. aime ma ville.

d. J'   4. une gare.

e. Il y a une   5. place.

f. ...car elle est   6. France.

g. J'habite en   7. jolie

a	b	c	d	e	f	g
4						

155

5. Rock Climbing
Starting from the bottom, pick one chunk from each row to translate the sentences below.

a.	b.	c.	d.	e.
et une cathédrale.	mais il y a un supermarché.	n'y a pas de cinéma.	et un château.	et une piscine.
car il	de centre sportif,	une bibliothèque	un stade	Il y a une jolie place
dans ta ville?	il y a	il n'y a pas	mon quartier	il y a
Dans mon quartier	Dans ma ville	Dans mon village	Qu'est-ce qu'il y a	Je n'aime pas

a. In my neighbourhood, there is a library and a castle.

_____

b. In my town, there is a stadium and a cathedral.

_____

c. In my village, there isn't a sports centre, but there is a supermarket.

_____

d. What is there in your town? There is a pretty square and a swimming pool.

_____

e. I don't like my neighbourhood because there isn't a cinema.

_____

6. Fill in the gaps

a. Salut! Je m'appelle Stefano. J'ai _____ ans. Je viens d' _____, mais j'habite à Londres. J'aime ma ville car elle est très _____. Dans mon _____, il y a une _____ et ____ stade.

grande	Italie	neuf	un	quartier	piscine

b. Salut! Je m'appelle Nancy. Je viens d'Amérique, mais _____ à Bordeaux. ___ aime ma ville car _____ il fait chaud. Dans ____ ville, _____ des temples et _____ des piscines.

normalement	J'	j'habite	il y a	aussi	ma

7. Tangled Translation

a. Write the French words in English to complete the translation.

Hello, je m'appelle Anne. Je viens d'*England* mais *I live* en Italie. *I speak Italian* et allemand. *In Italy*, normalement, *the weather is good.* Dans mon quartier, *there is* une boulangerie *and shops,* mais *there isn't a* gare.

b. Write the English words in French to complete the translation.

Bonjour! *My name is* Jorge. J'ai *twelve* ans. J'habite *in Germany*, dans la capitale qui s'appelle Berlin. *I like my town* car elle est *very big* et touristique. *In my* quartier, *there are* une pharmacie *and a shop,* mais il n'y a pas de *bakery*. Où habites-tu *and what* il y a *in your* ville?

8. Sentence Puzzle

Put the French words in the correct order.

a. quartier Dans mon des magasins il y a aussi des supermarchés. et

   In my neighbourhood, there are shops and also supermarkets.

b. Qu'est-ce qu' ta ville? Il y a il y a dans piscine une et place. une

   What is there in your town? There is a swimming pool and a square.

c. gare. cathédrale, une ville mais il n'y a pas de Dans ma il y a

   In my town, there is a cathedral but there isn't a train station.

d. jolie Ma ville car des restaurants il y a. et des magasins est

   My town is pretty because there are shops and restaurants.

9. Guided Translation

a. S_____! J__ m'a_____ M_____. J'h_____ d____ u__

j_____ v_____ q___ s'a_____ P_____.

Hi! My name is Mafalda. I live in a pretty town, which is called Paris.

b. J'h_____ d___ u__ j_____ v_____. D__ m__ v_____,

i__ y a d___ m_____, m___ i__ n'___ a p__ d__ p_____.

I live in a pretty town. In my town, there are shops but there isn't a

swimming pool.

c. D__ m__ q_____, i__ y a u__ é_____ et u__ é_____, m___

i__ n'___ a p__ d__ p_____. C'_____ t____ c_____.

In my neighbourhood, there is a school and a church, but there isn't a

park. It is very quiet.

158

 THE LANGUAGE GYM

10. Staircase Translation
Starting from the top, translate each chunk into French.
Write the sentences in the grid below.

a.	I like	my town.				
b.	I don't like	my town because	there isn't a cinema.			
c.	In my neighbourhood	there is a library but	there isn't a sports centre.	It is pretty.		
d.	In my town	there is a stadium but	there isn't a train station.	It is noisy	and also touristy.	
e.	In my town	there is a church but	there isn't a cathedral.	It is small	and also quiet	but it's ugly.

Answers / Réponses

a.	
b.	
c.	
d.	
e.	

🏆 Challenge / Défi
Can you create 2 more sentences using the words in the staircase grid above?

☆	
☆	

THE LANGUAGE GYM

No Snakes No Ladders

Unit 9-10

DÉPART	1 J'habite à...	2 J'habite à Barcelone.	3 mon village	4 ma ville	5 J'adore mon village.	6 Où habites-tu?	7 dans mon quartier
15 car elle n'est pas moche	14 Il est calme.	13 Elle est jolie.	12 J'aime ma ville car...	11 Il y a des magasins.	10 des parcs et des restau-rants	9 Il n'y a pas de centre sportif.	8 Il y a une piscine.
16 J'habite à Londres.	17 Mon village est bruyant.	18 Il y a un super-marché.	19 et une gare	20 Il y a aussi un parc.	21 Je déteste ma ville.	22 Mon village est petit.	23 J'habite à Paris.
ARRIVÉE	30 Ma ville est animée.	29 Mon village est animé.	28 car elle est grande	27 Je n'aime pas ma ville.	26 Il n'y a pas de cinéma.	25 un château et un musée	24 Il y a une église.

160

THE LANGUAGE GYM

No Snakes No Ladders

7 in my neighbour-hood	**8** There is a swimming pool.	**23** I live in Paris.	**24** There is a church.			
6 Where do you live?	**9** There isn't a sports centre.	**22** My village is small.	**25** a castle and a museum			
5 I love my village.	**10** parks and restau-rants	**21** I hate my town.	**26** There isn't a cinema.			
4 my town	**11** There are shops.	**20** There is also a park.	**27** I don't like my town.			
3 my village	**12** I like my town because...	**19** and a train station	**28** because it is big (f)			
2 I live in Barcelona.	**13** It is pretty. (f)	**18** There is a super-market.	**29** My village is lively.			
1 I live in...	**14** It is quiet. (m)	**17** My village is noisy.	**30** My town is lively.			
DÉPART	**15** because it is not ugly (f)	**16** I live in London.	ARRIVÉE			

161

The End

We hope you have enjoyed using this workbook and found it useful!

As many of you will appreciate, the penguin is a fantastic animal. At Language Gym, we hold it as a symbol of resilience, bravery and good humour; able to thrive in the harshest possible environments, and with, arguably the best gait in the animal kingdom (black panther or penguin, you choose).

There are several penguins (pictures)in this book. Did you spot them all?

If you enjoyed this book, why not continue on to Part 2 – available on Amazon and via direct order at **language-gym@piefke-trading.com**

THE LANGUAGE GYM

Printed in Great Britain
by Amazon

81377372R00099